DATE DUE

The Indestructible Commodore Matthew Perry

BORN: April 10, 1794

DIED: March 4, 1859

Matthew Perry became a midshipman at sixteen, determined to be as good a naval officer as his father and brothers. He proved his courage in attacks on pirates from the Everglades to the African Gold Coast and in the war with Mexico. A pioneer of naval education and sanitation, his struggle to modernize our navy earned him the title of Father of the Steam Navy. A gifted diplomat, he served in Russia, Tripoli, Africa, and his crowning achievement was breaking through Japanese isolation and affecting the first trade treaty with the United States. This is the exciting story of an indestructible man whose courage, wisdom and devotion to his country influenced the course of history.

The Indestructible Commodore Matthew Perry

by
Arthur Orrmont

 Julian Messner, Inc. · New York

Published by Julian Messner, Inc.
8 West 40 Street, New York 18

Published simultaneously in Canada
by The Copp Clark Publishing Co. Limited

Second Printing, 1962

Printed in the United States of America
Library of Congress Catalog Card No. 62-10195

To My Mother

ACKNOWLEDGMENT

The author is grateful to Rear Admiral E. M. Eller, U.S.N., Director of Naval History, and to his assistants in the Navy Library and Naval Section, National Archives, Washington, D.C., for making available to him valuable source material used in the writing of this book.

1 ——⟨⟨⟨⟨⟨⟨⟨⟨⟨⟨⟨⟨⟨⟨⟨⟨⟨⟨⟨⟨c

THE HOT SUN OF JUNE, 1807, SHONE DOWN ON NEWPORT
Harbor, minting flashes of gold from the blue water of Narragansett Bay.

A curly-headed, slightly-built boy of thirteen dressed in
singlet and knee breeches, leaned against the baywall. Books
lay helter-skelter on the cobblestones at his feet: the Bible,
Euclid and Noah Webster's speller. Matthew Calbraith Perry,
known at home as Cal, was on his way home from school. He
was also at his favorite pastime, roaming and mooning
about the harbor.

Off to his right, extending to the skyline beyond Point
Judith, where the Perry house overlooked the sea, were anchored the pride of American shipping—sloops and brigs and
schooners of draft both narrow and wide. Their brass was
polished, their clean windows winked back sunlight, their
decks shone white from hollystoning. But Cal Perry had little
interest in them. Instead he stared with fascination straight
before him at the waterlogged, rotting hulk lying half-sub-
merged in twenty feet of bay water.

To him this was no ordinary wreck. To him this pile of
decaying ship's timbers was hardly an eyesore to be towed
away, as some of the town fathers had recommended. These
were the remains of Captain Cook's famous ship *The Dis-*

11

covery. What strange shores it had touched under Captain Cook, greatest of Britain's maritime explorers—the Sandwich Islands, Alaska, Cape Prince of Wales, Siberia, even! While he himself had sailed no further than Providence, Rhode Island, in a dinghy.

Unfamiliar lands had always cast a spell of enchantment over Cal. How much more fun school would be, he often thought, if he could spend his time studying geography instead of Mr. Webster's tiresome vocabulary. Maps, with their mysterious, unexplored areas called "terra incognita" were so much more interesting than rules set down in a book. To sail away under clouds of billowing sail to unknown lands where adventure waited—that was the life for a boy; the life for a man too!

His elation ended in a frown. A career at sea wasn't too likely for him, if he listened to what his eldest brother, Oliver, told him. "Cal," the dashing, romantic midshipman had said, "you're not cut out to be a sailor. You're cautious as a cobbler and shy as a mouse. Better concentrate on your sums and plan to settle down in a mercantile house. In the Navy it's the firebrands like father and me who win the gold braid and the glory."

With vicious suddenness a chunk of flung cobblestone struck Cal squarely in the back, and he gasped with the pain.

"Look at the Over-the-Point gentleman lollygaggin' at the wreck! Ain't he somethin' in them fancy Boston clothes?"

He turned to face two tough wharf rats in torn breeches and ragged shirts. There was hatred in their eyes. In Newport a deadly war was being fought between the "wharf rats" and the "Over-the-Point gentlemen." Until now Cal had managed to steer clear of the lower town ruffians, or had been accompanied by his brothers when he came down to the bay area. Now he stood alone, and he was scared.

His heart beat like a muster drum. He didn't like physical pain, he never had. For a moment it seemed to him Oliver was right. He would never make a fighting man, willing and able to stand up to canister and grape, not when a couple of bullies could make his knees knock.

The wharf rats came a threatening step closer. "What do you want?" Cal asked, his voice shrill with tension.

The smaller of the two mimicked him maliciously. "He says what do we want, Johnny. Well, let's tell him we aim to pull out that pretty girl's hair of his, bloody his nose, and bust a rib or two." He laughed, and Cal's face turned white.

Craftily the bigger wharf rat observed the frightened, well-dressed boy. "We'll settle for the money in your pocket," he said. "Give it here and we'll let you be." He balled his hamlike fists in menace.

Looking around him, Cal saw that the baywalk was deserted. Though he despised himself for it, there seemed nothing to do but hand over the silver dollar with which he had planned to buy a birthday present for his little sister Jane. To refuse them would mean a beating. The taller of the roughnecks was at least sixteen and had the shoulders of a blacksmith's apprentice, while the shorter one hefted a deadly billy. The head of more than one "Over-the-Point gentleman" had been cracked with such a weapon.

Now the wharf rats were only three or four paces away. "All right," Cal said, and reached into his pocket.

He looked down at what lay in the palm of his hand. It wasn't the silver dollar—that was in his other pocket. It was the lieutenant's hat insignia his brother Raymond, also a midshipman, had sent him from his ship the *Norfolk*.

The silver-threaded badge glittered in the sun. Assuming it was a coin, the smaller boy darted out his hand.

Something happened to Cal Perry then. Call it pride or call it sudden courage—it was both of these and something

13

more. What he held in his hand was a badge of rank in the United States Navy. One day he hoped to wear it. His father, Christopher Perry, had worn the insignia of a lieutenant in one of the bloodiest sea battles of the Revolution, when the *Trumbull* fought his Majesty's ship *Watt*. Oliver would soon sail as a senior grade lieutenant, and so, eventually, would Raymond. Calbraith Perry came from a family of seafarers, of Navy men bred to salt air and a rolling deck.

He knew, sure as he stood there on Newport baywalk, that if he gave this bit of silver thread to the thieves who demanded it, there would be no Lieutenant Matthew Calbraith Perry to wear it sewed to his hat. If he gave it up, he would never be fit to be an officer in the service of his country.

It had taken only a moment for these thoughts to rush through his head, but in that time the smaller wharf rat had him by the arm and was prying his fingers open. Cal lashed out in inspired fury. His fist struck the boy in the windpipe, and he fell sprawling to the cobbles, choking for air.

Cursing, the other boy rushed forward. Cal sidestepped, and the wharf rat ran heavily into the wall. Before he could turn, Cal picked up the billy dropped by his confederate, now rising groggily to his feet.

"You'll give me that money but I'll half kill you first!" the big boy shouted, and went for him.

Cal didn't hesitate to use the club against his enemy's superior muscle and strength, but the contest was an unequal one. The billy was quickly wrested from him. He had to contend with fists punishing his body and face, and kicks from the smaller boy, who by now had recovered.

"Somebody's coming!" the smaller boy yelled. "Let's go!"

Suddenly relieved of the oppressive weight upon him, Cal heard his attackers scuttling down the baywalk.

He looked up into a whiskered face peering into his own.

"Why, it's Cap'n Perry's boy! What happened, lad, the wharf rats get you?"

Cal nodded, and with the seaman's help got to his feet. He wasn't badly hurt, only scratched, bruised and dizzy. But no seamstress could mend the tears in his shirt and breeches, and his mother would have something sharp to say about that.

"Looks like you fought 'em off. Your brother Oliver would be proud, lad. Here, I'll brush you off. Sure you don't need help to home?"

"No, but thanks just the same."

Limping a little, Cal started off when the seaman called him back and handed him the billy. "A souvenir," he grinned. "You won it fair and square."

On Truro Street people smiled at his disheveled look, but he paid them no mind. In one of the shops he bought a cambric handkerchief and asked that the gift package be tied with a ribbon. At home, Jane greeted him with a shriek, but soon became absorbed in her present. His mother came into the room and rapped out a brisk command for him to wash and change. Later, he knew, she would demand an explanation.

Cal was spared a lecture, at least for the moment. As he dried his face on the huck towel, his father slammed into the house. Captain Christopher Perry had news of a battle much more important than any Newport street fight.

When Cal slipped into the sitting room, his father, handsome face flushed, had just pounded his fist on the mahogany table. A candlestick wobbled dangerously, and Sarah Perry watched it with a housewife's anxious concern.

"I tell you," he said angrily, "no British ship has the right to stop and search an American ship for deserters. As if British impressment of American sailors wasn't bad enough.

15

If we had a Navy of any decent size, such an outrage never would have happened!"

Cal came up to his father's chair. "What outrage, sir?" His eyes were bright. "Does it look like war?"

His eyes still flashing, Captain Perry explained that many British tars had been deserting to the American Navy for its better food and treatment. Three of these deserters had been aboard the frigate *Chesapeake* when H.M.S. *Leopard* had stopped the American ship outside the international boundary and demanded return of the men. The *Chesapeake* refusing, the British ship had opened fire, causing several casualties. In no condition to fight a superior adversary, the American ship had been forced to hand over the deserters. What made the situation worse was that these men were originally American seamen impressed by the British.

"War's coming sooner than we think," the Captain said, "and unless that skinflint Congress loosens up on its pursestrings, our Navy won't be ready for it."

Cal swallowed hard. Now that war seemed closer, he wanted desperately to ask his father to apply for his midshipman's warrant. But he let the thought die for his father was staring hard at him. "Cal, those look like cuts and bruises. Were you fighting?"

"Yes, sir."

"Tell me about it." Contrary to what Cal expected, his father didn't seem at all displeased.

Cal was a truthful boy but a reticent one, and it was torture for him to tell the Captain exactly what had happened that afternoon. He mumbled and stumbled, and Mrs. Perry, aware of his embarrassment, tactfully left the room. Then, his face growing redder with every word, Cal came out with it. When he was through the Captain put his big hand gently on his son's shoulder.

"Cal, you know the story of my escape from the prison ship *Jersey* during the Revolution?"

He nodded, though he knew little about the Revolution or the part his father had played in it, having been born in 1794. Now he wondered miserably what this had to do with his confession of cowardice.

"You know pretty much what happened, but I don't think I've ever told you how I felt about it. Well, it wasn't bravery and it wasn't patriotism that made me strike down that guard from behind so that I and twenty others could escape over the side."

"No, sir?" Cal asked respectfully, though he doubted it very much. His father and Oliver were the heroes of the family.

"No, it wasn't courage. You see, over six thousand men died aboard the *Jersey* during the war, from rotten food, disease and malnutrition."

Cal frowned, not quite getting the point.

"If I didn't escape from the *Jersey* I knew I'd die there. What you did today was much braver. The coward thinks only of himself in a crisis, never of something better or greater than himself, as you did."

Always uncomfortable at praise, Cal blushed violently.

"Before this, I confess," his father went on, "I agreed with your brother about one Matthew Calbraith Perry. I doubted if he was right for the Navy, and I thought him better suited to push a quill in some countinghouse. But I've changed my mind. Today I shall write Secretary Smith of the Navy Department asking for your warrant as midshipman. It's going to be a while till the appointment comes through—a year at least. But I daresay Cal Perry has a very good chance of being the youngest middie ever to be commissioned in the United States Navy!"

2

"STAND EASY!" SNAPPED CAPTAIN OLIVER HAZARD PERRY.

Though he ached with tension, Midshipman Matthew Calbraith Perry tried to appear relaxed before his brother, commanding officer of the 12-gun schooner *Revenge*.

From his seat behind the oak table the Captain, coldly eyed the slim apprentice officer. "I hear that the steerage is ringing with your juvenile complaints." There was no brotherly tolerance in his manner. "You find patrol duty boring, and Newport as a home base doesn't suit you."

Cal stared grimly straight ahead. He guessed he had been talking too freely about his dissatisfaction with the *Revenge*'s peaceful, humdrum routine. But some action, some adventure, were long overdue. He had waited a year and a half for his commission, only to be sent to the naval station in New York for weeks and weeks of routine duty. The tedious days spent in either drill or copying out documents had been bearable only because he knew assignment to a ship awaited all midshipmen, however long they marked time in New York.

Even after he had boarded the *Revenge*, to begin his actual training, Navy life had been painfully dull. In a year of quiet sailing from Long Island's Montauk Point to Nantucket Shoals and back again, they hadn't sighted a single

18

British ship. It was like an endless pleasure cruise, except that Cal Perry took no pleasure in it.

"In future," Captain Perry said, "you will bring all your criticisms directly to me."

"Aye, sir."

"And I will do exactly nothing about arranging a transfer for you from the *Revenge*. You're not here for excitement, but to learn. It's a full course—seamanship from the seamen, gunnery from the gunners, navigation from me. Chaplain Elliott tells me your astronomy and mathematics are good enough, but they're not all of what makes a naval officer."

"No, sir," Midshipman Perry said, and saluted smartly.

"I haven't finished. Remember, I don't want this crew infected by your girlish wailings." Captain Perry glanced with seeming significance at Cal's curly locks. "Do you understand?"

"*Aye, sir,*" Cal answered between his teeth, and returning his brother's salute, left the cabin.

When he got to his steerage quarters he was still trembling with rage. Midshipman James Johnson, asleep in his hammock, was rudely awakened by the kick Cal delivered at the wooden locker. He sat up, rubbing his eyes.

"What's the matter, Curly? Did you trade broadsides with His Majesty the Captain?" Though Captain Perry was admired by the men of the *Revenge* he was also feared.

"Don't call me Curly!" Cal said, smoothing down his hair in the quick, unconscious gesture that was to be characteristic of him for most of his life. With a quick shove he upset Johnson's hammock, and the middy dropped like a stone to the planking.

The sight of the spread-eagled Johnson, all flailing arms and legs, somewhat improved Cal's temper. Grinning, he helped Johnson to his feet, and took a seat beside him on the locker.

19

"Tell me about it, Cal," the midshipman said.

Cal's grin faded. "There weren't any broadsides to trade," he said bitterly. "My guns were spiked early in the fight, and His Majesty shot down my mainmast with a single volley." His eyes darkened with resentment. "But he hasn't made me strike my colors, Jimmy, never! I'll see Tunis, and Singapore and Marseilles before I die. Not even Oliver Hazard Perry can prevent that!"

"But why should the Captain be so mean to you?" Johnson asked. "After all, you're his brother."

"But that's exactly why, Jimmy," Cal explained. "You can be meaner to somebody in your family than to anybody else. Oliver's never thought I was right for the Navy and he never will. He thinks only someone who can knock down a man twice his size belongs on the deck of a frigate. Because I look more like a scholar than a sailor he just won't believe I belong."

"But you're so good with the sextant," Johnson protested, "and with figures, and the other day at gunnery—"

"Oliver told me those three targets I hit in gunnery practice were just plain luck. If I happen to be good at astronomy and mathematics, to him it means I'm a book sailor, no more than that. The worst of it's navigation. Oliver's my teacher, and when he asks me a question I just freeze up."

"Why not ask your father to get you a transfer?"

"The trouble is," Cal groaned, "that Father agrees with Oliver, though for different reasons. With war threatening now he thinks I'd do better learning to tar a plank than sail a junk off China. And Mother's always after him to keep me safe. She's afraid I'll end up in a British prison ship."

Midshipman Johnson was a young man not too familiar with the frustrating powers of authority, but he knew determination when he saw it. He put his arm comfortingly around Cal's shoulder. "Don't worry," he said. "You'll get off the *Revenge*. I know it."

It took another six months and a score of letters home to Captain Perry, but Midshipman Johnson's prediction proved accurate. The Captain heard of a vacancy on the *President*, one of the finest ships of the infant Navy, and he finally gave in and used his influence to arrange a transfer. On a brisk October afternoon in 1810, shortly after Cal Perry's sixteenth birthday, Lieutenant Raymond Perry welcomed his brother aboard Commodore Samuel Rodgers' 56-gun flagship for duty in the Atlantic Coast squadron.

A few months later, Cal was tarring a plank on the *President*'s berth deck when he heard his first news of the *Revenge*. It made him grind his teeth for missed excitement. Oliver's ship had been blown ashore in a sudden gale and sunk off the Rhode Island coast. Fortunately no lives had been lost in the disaster.

But Cal's regret passed quickly. Life aboard the flagship, for all its menial chores, had its own drama and interest. The *President* cruised much further than the *Revenge* had, up and down the entire seaboard. There were constant gun drills and practice calls to general quarters, often in the middle of the night. Breaking out the heavy ammunition quickly was a challenge, and good for the muscles. He was thriving on the active shipboard life, gaining weight and shooting up so alarmingly that the quartermaster grumbled about the alterations necessary on his uniforms.

The only thing he would have changed was the harsh discipline. The entire ship jumped to toe the mark for Commodore Samuel Rodgers, whom it was impossible to please, and sometimes the men were lashed for what seemed to Cal trifling misdemeanors.

One day Cal got his first taste of Commodore Rodgers'

temper when he was on watch duty, pacing that part of the deck which roofed the Commodore's cabin.

"Midshipman Perry!" someone shouted, and Cal turned to face an irate Rodgers with fire in his eye.

"Aye, sir," Cal said quakingly, wondering what on earth he could have done wrong. If he had missed a sail on the horizon, why hadn't it been reported by the crow's-nest?

"Your tread, sir," the Commodore said sarcastically, "is as heavy as a seventy-gun bombardment. For the life of me I can't keep my mind on the log. Hand me that glass."

Obeying, Cal noticed that a number of officers and seamen had turned to stare. Some hid smiles.

"I'll take your post, sir," the Commodore said, "and you'll go below to my cabin to hear how loud a pair of over-proud boot heels can sound!"

Stunned, Cal stood there rooted to the spot.

"Below, and quick about it!"

If his heels had been heavy before, now they were light. He scurried down to the Commodore's cabin faster than he had ever covered the same distance in a call to general quarters. There, for the next half hour, he listened to Rodgers' ponderous tread as the Commodore mocked his own self-important pacing. Sitting in the Commodore's chair gave him gooseflesh, and it took great effort to keep his eyes away from the list of recommended promotions on Rodgers' desk.

Later, his ordeal over, Cal was welcomed back to the steerage with hoots of laughter. But the Commodore must have been impressed with the caliber of his work, for a week after his seventeenth birthday, in his second year on the *President,* Cal was made a personal aide. Brother Raymond was first to offer his congratulations.

The war Christopher Perry had said was coming was closer now. High officers came often to confer with Rodgers on the flagship, and Cal was kept busy arranging for their receptions. Impressment of American sailors into British ranks was more flagrant now than ever, and in May, 1811, grave dispatches from the capital were delivered to the *President* in Chesapeake Bay. A British warship, the *Guerriere*, had stopped an American merchant ship at the very entrance to New York harbor and forcibly abducted two seamen. The *President* was ordered to sail immediately and intercept the marauder.

However, Commodore Rodgers was visiting his home in Maryland, and the flagship could not sail without him. Raymond Perry called his brother to the wardroom and gave him command of the gig that would row seventy miles to Havre de Grace, pick up the Commodore, and return him to the ship.

It was no easy assignment. All that night and the following day the small boat splashed along the shore, every man in turn sweating at the oars until he dropped from exhaustion. Cal raised huge blisters on the palms of his hands. One oarsman fell to the scuppers, crimson gushing from his nose. He had burst a blood vessel. At twilight the boat pulled into shore.

When Cal returned with a puffing Commodore Rodgers, the whipped oarsmen pushed off at once for Chesapeake Bay. A breeze came up and a sail was hoisted. They sighted the flagship late the next afternoon.

Commodore Rodgers smiled at his young pilot in the bow. "Well done, Mr. Perry. No doubt this trip will receive prominent mention in your journal." It was Cal's job to keep the ship's journal, a more general record than the ship's log.

Cal nodded absently, his mind on more important things. "Sir," he asked, "do you think we'll catch up with the enemy?" He meant the *Guerriere*.

"Luck and the winds, Mister. Pray for them, hard, and we shall see."

In ten days Cal's wish was granted, though not with the *Guerriere*. South of Sandy Hook the *President's* lookout sighted a strange sail, and though it wasn't the class of ship to which the *Guerriere* belonged, the ship was most likely British.

On the *President* the ensign and pennant were raised, and the crew beat to quarters. At dusk Commodore Rodgers came to within half a cable length of the unidentified ship. From the quarter-deck, Cal saw that it carried twenty-two guns.

"What ship are you?" hailed Rodgers.

From across the water came the same query.

Before the Commodore could answer, the stranger fired a shot over the *President's* gun deck. The American gunners returned the compliment with a single shot. The hostile ship replied with three more cannon shots and a scattering of musket fire. A musket ball whined over Cal's head and died at sea.

The young midshipman crouched down on the quarter-deck beside George Slidell, one of his fellow apprentice officers. Cal was trembling; any moment, he was sure, his teeth would begin to chatter. "You're not going to be afraid," he told himself. "This is your first battle and it means a lot. You've got to be as brave as—Oliver."

It was a comfort to see that George, usually the most unconcerned of mortals, was more scared than he. The midshipman's face was a sickly green.

"It's all right," Cal told him stoutly, "our gunners are a lot better than theirs."

George shivered. "That's all very well, but they've got more than twenty guns. I'd rather it was ten—wouldn't you?"

"General fire!" Rodgers ordered from the bridge. For fifteen minutes the two midshipmen flinched through the cannonading that shook the ship. When the Commodore ordered a cease fire, the enemy's guns had been silent for some minutes. It was plain she had gotten much the worst of the fight.

"She's falling away to leeward!" yelled Lieutenant Sanders, the executive officer. "Should we give chase?"

"The Britisher's been punished enough for her insolence," the Commodore said. "Light battle lanterns and examine damage."

At daybreak the crippled ship was still astern. Commodore Rodgers lowered a boat and sent Lieutenant Raymond Perry to investigate. He returned with the information that the ship was his Majesty's sloop-of-war *Little Belt,* Captain Bingham commanding.

The Commodore sighed. "If there was a war on she would have made a pretty prize. Signal permission to proceed."

There was no celebration that night in the steerage. To Cal and his fellow junior officers the *President's* failure to encounter the *Guerriere* was a bitter disappointment. But when news of the battle became known, the American public rejoiced—the humiliation of the *Chesapeake* in 1807 had been avenged. Yankee seamen had shown proud Britain it could no longer willfully seize American ships and impress American sailors.

When he went home on leave, all Cal heard in Newport was threats against the British. Christopher Perry flatly predicted war next year. He was right. President Madison declared war against Britain on June 12, 1812.

The *President* took part in the first hostilities. In late June Cal was returning to the forecastle deck from an errand to the wardroom, when the crow's-nest sighted a British frigate off Nantucket Shoals. The ship was called to general quarters. Cal was adjusting his glass on the Englishman's pennon when the Commodore came up and trained his own telescope on the distant sail.

25

"Too bad we're traveling in squadron," the Commodore said. "If the *Congress*, the *Argus* and the *United States* weren't with us that Britisher might fight, but odds of four to one are too much for her. She'll head straight for Halifax, and haven."

"But sir, we're the fastest ship in the squadron," Cal protested. "Can't we leave the others behind and try to cut her off?"

A grin crossed the Commodore's weathered face. "We are, Mister Perry, and we will."

It took the entire afternoon to catch up with the British ship, and Cal chafed at the exasperating delays he was learning were the greater part of action at sea. But by 4:30 the *President*'s long guns were brought to bear on the frigate. Cal could see the name *Belvidera* lettered in gold on her bow. She was about a half mile away.

He felt as nervous now as he had in last year's encounter with the *Little Belt*, his baptism of fire. Now the Englishman's guns seemed to point directly at his stomach, and he shivered. At eighteen life was very sweet.

He stood with Commodore Rodgers at the forecastle gun, ready to run messages for him once the battle had begun. The Commodore held the lighted match, and Cal stared in fascination at the spitting flame. He had discharged cannon himself in practice, but things were different now. This was war, and the firing of this gun might result in the death of many men, his own included.

Rodgers dipped the match. The roar deafened Cal and almost burst his eardrums, but then, pain and discomfort forgotten, he was following the Britisher through his glass.

"A hit, sir!" he shouted. "Square in her stern!"

Another officer confirmed the damage. Cal's pulse raced as the *President*'s main gun was discharged, disabling the *Belvidera* further. When the sound of the third blast had faded, he reported on the further heavy damage to Rodgers. One of the deck officers commented that with another such shot the prize would be theirs.

Cal was leaving the forecastle with a message for the gun deck when there was a tremendous explosion. The deck heaved under his feet and he was thrown against the bulkhead. Commodore Rodgers rose high into the air and landed with his leg twisted beneath him. For a moment Cal was blinded by the pall of smoke, and then, near the companionway, he saw Midshipman Taylor slumped on the shattered planking. Blood streamed from a terrible wound in the boy's side.

An arrow of pain stabbed through Cal's thigh as he lifted himself to his hands and knees. He looked down at the patch of red seeping through his white trousers. But he could move his leg, and evidently no bones were broken.

Limping to Taylor's side, he gently turned the midshipman over. He was dead.

Lieutenant Sanders knelt anxiously by the white-faced Commodore, who was groaning with pain. "Go below for the doctor!" Sanders flung at Cal, not noticing his wound. "The Commodore's broken his leg."

Midshipman Perry stumbled down the companionway to the surgery, almost fainting with the effort. The assistant surgeon, busy preparing to receive the wounded, told Cal his chief had already gone to the forecastle to tend Rodgers. Then he saw the blood on Cal's white duck trousers. "You're a brave one! Why didn't you tell me? Here, sit down. We've got to bandage that wound."

You're a brave one. A man who knew bravery when he saw it had called him courageous!

Though he had lost a certain amount of blood, the doctor gave him permission to return to his quarters. Back in the steerage, Cal heard the outcome of the battle from the junior

27

officers. When the wind came up the British ship made every effort to escape and her crew threw everything from stores to extra spars overboard. The *Belvidera* had managed to hold her distance, and when the wind fell the *President* abandoned the chase.

Midshipman Gifford's forehead creased gloomily. "Now the *Belvidera* will get to Halifax with news that war's been declared, and we'll lose our chance of surprise."

"What do we care about surprise?" an apprentice officer said stoutly. "We'll lick 'em anyway."

"Fool!" another junior officer broke in, "Don't you know the British have twenty ships to our one?"

At hot argument began over the fighting merits of Englishman and Yankee, and Cal, who thought uninformed debate a waste of time, took out his pen and ink and journal. One of the midshipman glanced over his shoulder as he wrote, and the boy's eyes widened in surprise. "But Perry, you didn't mention your wound! If I'd been hurt I'd write about it—at least two pages worth."

"Perry's too modest," one of the others said.

"Unlike his brother Oliver," said Midshipman Gifford, who was known for his unkind wit.

Cal threw down his pen and glared at Gifford. "My brother doesn't bear criticism from the likes of you! Watch your tongue!" Nobody was going to speak slurringly of Oliver unless it was himself. He might not get along with his brother, but the Perrys always stood together against the outside world.

Gifford wanted no fight with the wounded hero. He smiled tightly in the silence. "Have it your way. I daresay we'll be needing some immodestly reckless fellows in the days to come."

The squadron anchored in Boston Harbor for a month's overhauling. In a week Cal's wound had healed. Bored with the inactivity, he went to Commodore Rodgers with a suggestion. Why not open a recruiting office in the city with himself in charge? Pleased with his zeal, Rodgers agreed, and Cal set up headquarters on Beacon Street.

Dissatisfied with the old and gaudy enlistment methods of flag-waving and fife-tooting, he introduced a new one of his own. Likely male passersby were intercepted on the sidewalk and invited inside for a brief chat about the great United States Navy. The chat always developed into a lengthy lecture, unless the prospect managed to bolt before.

One such victim was accompanied by a pretty young girl whose effect on Cal was disturbing. The young recruiter offered his guests chairs and launched into a glowing tribute to the Navy of John Paul Jones and Samuel Rodgers. But the girl's blonde ringlets and pert, uptilted nose made it hard for him to keep his mind on his work. Her eyes, sparkling with a mischievous laughter, he felt were directed at him. Did she consider him too young for such important business? Nonsense. At eighteen a sailor was a man.

Finally Cal pushed the application form before the poker-faced civilian, asking, "Have I succeeded in interesting you in the service?"

"You have," the young man replied dryly, "except that I must tell you I am already a captain in the Army, at the moment on leave. I'm Edgar Warren, and this is my cousin Jane Slidell, visiting from New York."

Miss Slidell went off into peals of laughter, and a red-faced Cal stared at the pair.

"Forgive my cousin's laughter," Warren said, "but your attack was so sudden and your cannonading so steady that I had no chance to explain. Actually, all the younger Warrens and Slidells are serving their country. There's myself and my brother Thomas in the Army, and Jane's brother George is a midshipman with Commodore Rodgers."

29

"I know George," Cal told them, and introduced himself.

"George has spoken of you often," Jane Slidell said, throwing him a sidelong look that made his heart turn over. "He and the other midshipmen are quite jealous of Matthew Perry. It seems the Commodore thinks more highly of this gentleman than any other junior officer in the squadron."

Tactfully ignoring Cal's embarrassment, Edgar Warren pushed back his chair. "We must be going to our lecture at the Atheneum. But perhaps you will join us for dinner next week. Are you free Tuesday?"

Cal accepted quickly and saw them to the door, feeling slightly dizzy. For the rest of the afternoon it was hard to concentrate on his enlistment report.

Tuesday at the Warrens he barely touched his excellent dinner. Making polite conversation afterward in the parlor, with Jane sitting beside him, was worse than facing an enemy's broadside. There seemed no way he could get her alone long enough to arrange another meeting.

It was Jane herself who managed it. As he was leaving she asked if that week end he would like to come out to the Warren's farm on the outskirts of Boston. "There isn't anything to do but ride in the surrey and feed the chickens," she smiled apologetically, "but if you want to get away from the ship for a while—"

"Oh, I would that," Cal blurted out. "I think surrey riding's fine and I like to feed the chickens, too."

That night, returning dazedly to the ship, he ran into a lamppost and blacked his eye. The first officer asked sternly if he'd been fighting, and sent him to the galley for a beefsteak.

The week end at the farm was delightful, and in the following weeks he saw Jane as often as duty allowed. They walked on the Common, chaperoned by the Warren's Negro slave in his blue livery, and had tea in Copley Square. One evening he took her to a play. In it the heroine's family objected to her marrying a naval officer. Afterward, riding back to the Warrens' in the brougham, Jane discussed the problem.

"I don't know why there was all that fuss," she said. "Why shouldn't the girl marry a sailor? A sailor's as good as a lawyer or a doctor any day."

"A sailor's at sea a lot," Cal answered nervously.

"But think how glad his wife is to see him when he does come home," she said with seeming innocence. "Such a marriage could never be a dull one."

Cal cleared his throat. "Would you—er, marry a sailor?"

"If I cared for him," Jane said softly, and took his hand.

Before the squadron left Boston he and Jane had confessed their love. If his promotion came through as expected, Cal would speak to her parents in New York next year, when she turned seventeen.

Jane came down to see him off. Her figure, dwindling on the dock as the ship left the harbor, made his heart catch in his throat.

For the ambitious midshipman with marriage on his mind, the year of 1813 wasn't as much adventure as plain hard work, meant to impress Commodore Rodgers with his abilities as an officer. Looking for British prizes, the Commodore sailed as far as Norway. Cal, sent ahead in a cutter to find a pilot, was probably the first American naval officer to land on the Norwegian coast and break bread with its hearty fishermen.

On the return trip to Newport a British schooner bore down on the *President* off Nantucket Shoals. To confuse her, Rodgers hoisted the Union Jack. In return the schooner signaled: "Are you H.M.S. *Seahorse*?"

Cal grinned as the Commodore signaled that he was indeed the *Seahorse*. Then the wily Yankee invited the British captain aboard.

With four other delighted middies, including George Slidell, Cal listened outside Rodgers' cabin window as the Englishman explained his presence off the American coast.

"We're after Rodgers," he said, sipping his port. "The crafty old fish has escaped our net so far, but we'll get him yet. Have you ever seen the man?"

"Never," said Rodgers, "but I hear he's devilishly hard to catch. Much harder than yourself, sir."

The British captain looked politely bewildered, and Rodgers said finally, "You, sir, are aboard the U.S.S. *President* and talking to that crafty old fish himself. May I offer you another glass of port while my prize crew boards your ship?"

Cal guffawed and George Slidell clapped a hand against his mouth to quiet his own laughter; the others fled down the deck, holding their sides. It was hard to say what startled the Englishman more, his neat capture without the firing of a shot, or the burst of merriment from outside the cabin window.

Despite its prize the *President* got little attention when it docked in Narragansett Bay. Something much more important had happened recently to excite the town of Newport. Cal heard the news from the wharfsmen, from townspeople who stopped him as he made his way up the hill to Point Judith, from his parents as they greeted him at the door.

Oliver Hazard Perry had won the battle of Lake Erie. Off Amherstburg he had defeated the British squadron under Captain Barclay in the most decisive victory of the war.

"The whole country's agog with it," his sister Jane chattered as Cal sipped a cup of tea, unnoticed in the parlor filled with visiting notables come to do honor to his brother.

"Isn't Oliver the handsome hero though? And look at all the people—it's been like this for days now."

Oliver was indeed the handsome hero, with his black flashing eyes and confident look, his assurance of the conqueror. Midshipman Perry set down his cup, and waited till his brother had a chance to welcome him home. Half an hour later the victor of Lake Erie came over and slapped Cal on the shoulder.

"A good cruise, Cal? Any action?" Oliver grinned, remembering their difficulties aboard the *Revenge*.

"Not nearly as much action as you. The whole Atlantic hasn't a tenth of the drama of Lake Erie. My congratulations."

"And mine to you. I hear you have a lovely lady, both well-connected and beautiful."

Christopher Perry interrupted, thrusting a letter into Cal's hand postmarked Washington. "It arrived this morning," he said casually, and took Oliver away to meet a new arrival of importance.

Cal's letter was from the Navy Department. He had been commissioned a junior lieutenant.

Now he and Jane could get married!

He wanted to tell his parents the good news, but they were busy with Oliver and the high Washington official. Raymond was talking to a Congressman. Cal would have told his sister Jane, but she had taken his young brother Alexander to the kitchen for something to eat.

He left the house for a solitary walk along the harbor.

Let Oliver have his great victory, he thought. His own personal triumph was, to him, a greater one.

3

FROM HIS SICKBED PILLOW CAL WATCHED THE LATE JANUARY snow coming down outside the bedroom windows of his and Jane's new little house on Boston Common. The thick flakes, blown by the wind and falling at random, were, he thought, as meaningless and unsubstantial as his current prospects. Here he was, laid low by pneumonia on the very day the *President* was sailing from Boston to raid British shipping in the romantic Caribbean. It was a fine time to be in bed; people were saying the war would be over by spring, and that didn't give him much time to make his reputation in it. He was so far behind Oliver that he didn't have the slightest chance of catching up to his illustrious brother unless the French came in on the American side and prolonged the war for another decade.

From the passageway he heard the sound of approaching footsteps and the trill of Jane's light laughter, and his mood brightened. At least he had taken as his prize, last Christmas Eve, the sweetest helpmate a naval officer could have. He should be grateful for that. He thought with a grin how much prettier Jane was than Elizabeth Perry, Oliver's wife. He should consider himself a very lucky young man indeed, and put a stop to all this stewing and fretting.

34

Jane Perry came into the room, followed by his brother Raymond. Cal sneezed in the momentary draft. Jane pulled up the covers and clucked at her young husband with wifely concern. She turned to Raymond. "Ray, I want you to make it clear to Cal that he might not ever get out of bed again unless he keeps himself warm."

Raymond laughed. "He's a lot warmer here than he'd be on the deck of the *President*."

"Speaking of decks," Cal said, "how is it you're not striding the *President*'s right now?

"I've been ordered to report to Warren, Rhode Island, next month, to recruit for the brigs we're building there. So has Commodore Oliver, when he gets back from Washington, and so have you and young Alexander."

Cal stared at Raymond, biting his lip. He was glad to be getting back to duty, but working under Oliver was another thing, and not at all to his liking. He would have preferred the worst tyrant in the Navy to his impatient, brilliant brother. At least, with a tyrant, he would have known where he stood. The explosive emotions of pride, rivalry and jealousy complicated his relationship with Oliver to an extreme degree, and whenever he and his brother were in the same state together, let alone the same shipyard, there was bound to be trouble.

"You don't seem too happy at the news," said Raymond slyly.

Cal was silent, and Jane rushed into the breach. "It's not that, Ray. Cal would rather be sailing on a man-of-war than pushing a quill at a recruiting station."

Raymond leaned forward earnestly. "Cal, your attitude is all wrong. You know how badly the British outnumber our Navy. The only time we're allowed to fight is when we're attacked and can't escape. If a squadron of our ships destroyed twenty British at the cost of three of ours, it would

35

still be a major disaster. We've got to have new ships and we've got to get crews for them. A recruiter who knows his job is just as valuable as a first class gunnery officer or navigator."

In the silence Jane turned to Raymond. "Is there any other news?"

"Oh, yes. Oliver's still on his triumphal tour, and we hear that the ball of honor they gave him in Baltimore was the biggest in the city's history. And Congress has given him a seat on the floor. Such a thing's never happened to a Navy man in American history."

Watching Cal's face light up with pride, Jane was glad her husband had the generosity and good will not to begrudge his famous brother all the hero's laurels he was winning. Cal might feel he was Oliver's rival, but there wasn't a mean bone in his body.

The brothers talked for a while longer about Oliver and Alexander, who now wore a midshipman's uniform, and then Jane, seeing that Cal was tiring, took Raymond out of the room.

Before he slept, Cal wondered what it must have been like for Oliver to lead Elizabeth at the Baltimore ball, to take his seat in Congress while scores of important and distinguished men stood to applaud. Would he gain half such fame in his lifetime? It wasn't very likely. And yet, he thought, fame really wasn't what he wanted most. What drove him more than the spur of rank and glory was the desire to do a better job than anybody else. He had a great, perhaps even a fanatical, desire to achieve perfection.

In the ragbag fleet that was the United States Navy such a drive would doubtless have little to work on. But Cal Perry didn't care; he guessed he would have been that way whether he'd gone into law, the ministry, or business. It was good he loved the Navy, very good, he thought drowsily, before he

36

drifted off into sleep, to dream of himself forcing the British admiral to strike his colors after the greatest sea battle ever fought. It was perhaps strange that the Britisher should have had Oliver Hazard Perry's high-bridged nose and sharp black eyes.

As he stood stiffly before his brother in the back office of the recruiting station on State Street in Warren, Rhode Island, Cal thought back to the time seven years ago on the *Revenge*, when Oliver had had him on the carpet. Although he stood on a concrete floor rather than on the boards of a ship's cabin, it could have been the same scene, except that he was twenty-one now, and a man, not a midshipman with salt water behind his ears. He was going to make Oliver realize that fact, if it killed him.

"Oh come now, Cal," Oliver said, "take that ramrod out of your spine. Relax. That's the trouble with you, you're all spit and polish, and serious as a judge. I might be your superior officer, but we're brothers, and there's no reason why we can't discuss this matter in a reasonable, intelligent way."

It was a fair-sounding speech, but Oliver was angry, as Cal could see from the tightness of his lips. And when Oliver was angry he wasn't exactly fair. When he lost his temper you could expect no justice from him, especially if you were Matthew Calbraith Perry, whom Oliver Perry believed did not and never would belong in the United States Navy.

"All right," Cal said, dropping into a chair, "I'm willing to be reasonable and intelligent."

If Oliver got the implication, that he himself was not so willing, he didn't show it. "I want to make one point perfectly clear," Commodore Perry said. "We need recruits badly, and we need them in a hurry. Not next year, or the year after that, but now. We can't pick and choose among them; if we do, we won't have a navy to fight with. Do you

37

realize that the complement of the *Chippewa* is ten men short, and that of the *Saranac* seven?"

"Yes, I do," Cal said.

Oliver restrained his temper with difficulty. "Then why, may I ask, did you reject Moses Jones?"

"I didn't think he'd make a sailor on a fighting man-of-war. He would have been crying for his mother on the second day at sea."

"He looked manly enough to me," Oliver said.

"I disagree," said Cal evenly. "In the future, if you wish me to refer all my rejections to you for approval I'll do so, but as officer in charge of recruiting for the *Chippewa*, I feel I have a right to use my own judgment."

The telltale red was coming into Oliver's cheeks, but for the moment he contained himself. "Now what about Henry Stoddard? I got a glimpse of him, and he seemed the kind of lad who could learn to climb the rigging with the best of them."

"He had shifty eyes," Cal said. "And I heard something about him from his last employer that made me think he couldn't be trusted to keep his fingers out of other men's lockers. I think you'll agree that a thief in the fo'c'sle is as bad for morale as a broadside at fifteen yards."

"A man doesn't have to be a Diogenes to defend his country," Oliver said, biting off the words. "At Lake Erie my best gunner had his ears cropped for theft, and the man who swung the best cutlass had once been under a charge of piracy. I guess you're too young to know it, brother, but the world isn't made up of saints, and the best fighter is often the first man at the rum barrel."

"What you're saying is true enough, Oliver," Cal said, "and I'd be the last to deny it. But I don't think it applies to either Jones or Stoddard. They would have been much more trouble than they were worth."

38

Oliver looked down at the sheet of paper in his hand. "How about Lemuel Harding? Six feet tall and the brawn of a blacksmith."

"Harding didn't want to be a sailor," Cal replied. "A born landlubber if I ever saw one. His dearest ambition was to get a red coat in his sights and pull the trigger. He wouldn't have been happy in the Navy. In six months time his name would have shown up on the deserters' list."

Oliver slammed his fist down on the desk. "Lieutenant Perry," he roared, "it's the Lord who predicts events, not a block-headed dunce who can't tell a man from a milksop! I won't have you trying out your fancy theories at my expense! As a recruiting officer your orders are to sign any able-bodied man who can put an 'x' under his name. In the future every man you reject will come before me for my final decision in the matter! Is that understood?!"

As Oliver spoke Cal rose from his chair; now he stood at attention. "Aye, sir," he said stiffly.

There were several knocks at the door.

"Come in!" shouted Oliver angrily.

The door opened and Raymond Perry rushed into the room. He was breathing hard.

"Out with it, Ray!" Oliver demanded. "What's happened?"

"News from New York!" Raymond gasped out. "Two days ago the H.M.S. *Favorite* docked at the Battery under a flag of truce. It brought news of the signing of the Treaty of Ghent almost two months before. The British realize they can't blockade us indefinitely. The war's over!"

Raymond looked at his brothers in amazement. Their faces showed no elation, only disappointment. Oliver felt no joy at the end of war because as a man of action he knew that in peacetime it was impossible to add to the lustre of a military name. For Cal the news brought no gladness either, for he saw in it the end of his hopes for excitement and the proving of himself, not only in Oliver's eyes but in his own.

Oliver got up and paced restlessly around the room, his altercation with Cal forgotten.

"Well," he said, "this throws my plans into a cocked hat. I guess the only war that's left is the one shaping up with the Barbary pirates. There's talk that we're sending an expedition to Tripoli to release the American prisoners being held there by the pasha. Not only will the pirates be a pretty poor excuse for a war, but I don't like fighting in a hot climate."

"I know what this does to my plans," Cal said dourly. "I can't take a chance on asking for duty in a war that might last a couple of months at the most. Now I'll have to ask for a furlough to go into the merchant service. It wouldn't be fair to ask Jane to live on a Lieutenant's pay indefinitely." He turned to Raymond. "Ray, what about you?"

Raymond shrugged. "As a bachelor I don't have to worry about supporting a family. I'll stay on with the *President,* or maybe I'll fight the pirates with Oliver and Alexander."

"Lucky dog," Cal said with envy.

One of Oliver's aides stuck his head in the door. "Lieutenant Perry," he said, addressing Cal, "there's a young man waiting in your office who wants to sign on for the *Chippewa.* He says he's afraid the war will be over before he has a chance to see any action."

Cal sighed. "Tell him it's too late, Ensign Bates. The war is over."

"Aye, sir," Bates said, and turned to leave. Then what Cal had just said registered, and forgetting where he was the ensign whooped with joy, and ran out to spread the word.

Oliver poured three glasses of water from the carafe on his desk and handed them around. "Sorry it's not port or sherry, gentlemen, but water's the strongest thing I have. What shall we drink to?"

"To victory?" asked Raymond.

Oliver shook his head. "That wouldn't be true. The war's ended in a stalemate, with neither side victorious. The only thing we've won is the right to sail the seas without the British seizing our ships at their will and whim. And we've paid a price for it—a staggering expense of men and money. Not only that, our coastal and foreign shipping are practically destroyed."

"At least we've learned one thing," Cal said.

"What's that?" asked Raymond.

"That if we're to survive as a nation we need more than the eighteen ships we had when this war started, and the handful we've got left. So, gentlemen, let's drink to that—to our glorious new Navy! May it be the greatest the world has ever seen!"

Solemnly the three brothers raised their glasses and drank.

Bad news followed the news of peace; two months later Christopher Perry died in his Newport home. At the time, Cal was in New York, looking over Robert Fulton's steam-powered ship for the protection of New York harbor. For some time now, ever since he had heard of Fulton's experiments, he had been fired by the vision of a steam Navy.

He returned to Boston in time for the funeral. He had loved his father and his grief was deep. But Jane had joyful news—he was going to be a father!

He left for New York again to see about a job in the Holland trade. It worked out well; he came back to Boston with the command of the brig *Chelsea*, due to leave for Rotterdam in a month's time. He had already received a two-year furlough from the Navy Department.

Cal comforted the weeping Jane at the dock as the *Chelsea*

prepared to weigh anchor. "It isn't as bad as all that," he told her. "I'll be back in three months. Would you rather I sailed to the Barbary Coast like Oliver, to fight the pirates?"

Jane shook her head tearfully.

"Then what are you afraid of?" Cal laughed. "That I'll eat too much Dutch cheese and get round as an Edam?"

"No, it isn't that. I have a feeling that when the baby's born you'll be in Holland, or at sea."

"The sailor's life," Cal chided her, "is a hard one on the wife and bairns." He clasped her to him fiercely in one last embrace, and then trotted up the gangplank. When the ship pulled out of the harbor, under full sail, Cal watched Jane's white handkerchief till it faded into a white speck and then disappeared.

He was in the merchant service for a year and a half, and in that time he got home to Boston only five or six times. Jane was right—he was away at the birth of their first child, John Slidell, but he did arrive a week later, bearing gifts. He brought with him enough Dutch cheese to last the Perrys a year.

His merchant career wasn't all cheese or the luxuries he bought for his family with his captain's pay. He had done a lot of thinking during the long voyages to Rotterdam, Amsterdam and back to Boston and New York—hardheaded, practical thinking. It had occurred to him that the job of the emerging American Navy was a bigger one than merely acting as the protector of the American shores, important as that was; the Navy could also function as the spearhead of American commerce. America couldn't take her place among the leading nations of the world unless she was powerful and rich. He wrote several reports to the Navy Department on how it could help to expand American commerce, doubly so with the introduction of a fast steam Navy, but they were filed away to gather dust. Trade, his superiors said, was the responsibility of American merchants, a class for whom they lacked sympathy. The old sea dogs were interested in discipline, battle tactics, and exploration—certainly not in innovations.

Oliver, who was back from Tripoli, which had finally been forced to cease its attacks on American shipping, agreed with Cal's superiors. "Where's your sailor's spirit?" he asked his brother gruffly. "You should be thinking about more manly things than trade and profits. Leave such to the fat-bellied merchants and businessmen."

Cal kept his temper. "What more manly things do you speak of?" he asked quietly.

"You've got eyes," Oliver snapped. "Take the situation in South America, where these privateers are seizing all the shipping they can get their hands on—French, Spanish, British and American. There's a job for a man—putting a stop to it!"

Cal knew Oliver was soon to leave for Venezuela aboard the *John Adams* under the orders of the State Department. He also was fully aware that Oliver hadn't asked him to come along.

"Maybe I would have wanted to go to Venezuela with you, Oliver," he told him now, "if you'd asked me."

"The crew's made up," Oliver said curtly. "Besides, your constitution wouldn't take it. That's bad fever country."

Cal knew his health was better than his brother's, but he decided to let the comment pass. Oliver would never think he had the makings of a real sailor, and there was no way to change his mind about it.

Lieutenant Perry's reports to the Navy Department didn't absorb all his time and energy during this period of enforced inaction. He found himself becoming interested in a subject which fascinated many: the proposed establishment, on the African west coast, of a settlement for American free

43

Negroes. He would have been the first to admit, however, that it was the enthusiasm of the Reverend Jehudi Ashmun, one of the plan's leading spirits, that fired his own.

Ashmun, a young missionary and religious journalist, came to Boston to lecture on the proposed colony. Cal met him at the house of a mutual friend, and the two, taking to one another immediately, went off into a corner to talk.

Ashmun was confident that next year Congress would authorize the creation of a settlement to be called Liberia, under the auspices of the American Colonization Society, but he was frank in his description of the problems involved.

"The Colonization Society has two wings," he told Cal, "the northern and the southern. The northern wing hopes for an African colony which will eventually help to free the Negro from slavery in the United States by bringing free Negroes to Africa, where they will civilize their primitive brothers, thus making slavery less possible at the source. The southern wing, on the other hand, is afraid of the influence of the free Negro and hopes to get rid of that influence by sending *all* freedmen to an African colony or colonies. Thus we have two warring factions with different aims. I wonder," Ashmun went on, "if African colonization can be a success when we're split right down the middle this way."

"I've heard," said Cal, "that the southerners oppose using Liberia as a way station for cargoes of African slaves captured on the coast by antislavers."

Ashmun nodded. "Yes, that's still another problem." He smiled. "May I ask, Lieutenant, where your own sympathies lie—with the northern or the southern viewpoint?"

"With the northern," Cal answered. "I've never believed it was right for one man to own another."

Ashmun looked at him keenly. "I like you, Lieutenant Perry. And from what I've heard about your abilities and interests, I'm sure you can be of great value to us."

44

Cal blushed a little. "Of great value? How?"

"If Congress approves the creation of Liberia we'll be taking over the first shipload of free Negroes around the first of next year. How would you like to be an officer aboard one of the escort vessels? I think I could arrange it with the Navy Department."

"I'd consider it an honor."

"Your job wouldn't be exclusively escorting," Ashmun said. "Once they arrive off the Gold Coast the escort ships will undoubtedly begin cruising for outlaw slavers. I understand the slave ships don't hesitate to fire on their pursuers."

Cal grinned. "Africa and action too? I'd be a fool to refuse you."

Ashmun rose and held out his hand. "Then it's settled, Cal—if I may call you that?"

Cal gripped Ashmun's hand firmly. "Yes, Jehudi, it's settled." He smiled his boyish smile. "I'll ask my wife about it, but I'm sure she won't say no."

Six months later, in mid-1819, Congress authorized the creation of a colony in Africa under the direction of the American Colonization Society and ordered the Navy Department to provide an escort for the first immigrant ship. Ashmun was as good as his word; a week later Cal received his orders as a member of the expedition. He was to be executive officer under Captain Trenchard of the *Cyane,* a sloop-of-war that had been captured from the British in the War of 1812. The *Cyane* would convoy the brig *Elizabeth,* carrying eighty-eight free American Negroes on the pioneer voyage to Cape Mesurado. After the pilgrims were landed, the *Cyane* would then cruise the Gold Coast in search of slave ships, putting in at the new settlement whenever possible to give what help it could. Jehudi Ashmun was already at the colony and hard at work building makeshift quarters with a small staff. Cal had been able to meet with him several times before he left for Africa, and the two had become fast friends.

Life in the peacetime Navy was mostly waiting, and Lieutenant Perry was idle for still another five months till the expedition finally got under way. During that time Jane gave birth to Matthew junior, solacing them for the recent loss of their first born, John Slidell. The baby was beautiful and looked very much like the dead child, and when Cal remarked as much, Jane began to cry.

"Dear, we should be grateful," Cal told her. "It's as if God had given us Johnny back again."

"I'm not crying about that," Jane answered as she put the infant in its crib. "I'm just sad that the next time you see Matthew he'll probably be going on three years old."

Cal took her in his arms. "Nonsense," he joshed, though he felt as sad at the impending separation as she did. "You're just angry that I won't be here to help you change his diapers."

The *Cyane* sailed for Africa on a cold snowy day in February, 1820. The trip to the Gold Coast was an unhappy one. Not only did the *Elizabeth* leave three days before the *Cyane* did, in bad weather and pea-soup fog, but the brig seemed to have disappeared completely, and Captain Trenchard concluded that she had sunk in the heavy seas. When the *Cyane* arrived off Cape Mesurado in late March, Trenchard heard to his relief that the *Elizabeth* had called at Cape Verde a few days before. He finally caught up with her at Sherbro, the site for the new colony.

Like Captain Trenchard, Cal had been furious with the irresponsible officers of the *Elizabeth* who had sailed off without their escort, but when he heard of the ship's ordeal he was more disposed to sympathy. The Negroes, who knew nothing of the terrors of the sea, had been badly prepared for six weeks of storm, illness and despair. They had imagined that God would shield them from all unpleasantness, and when He seemed indifferent to their miseries, they had panicked. Discipline had become a mockery, and for a while the Negroes thought of mutinying, taking over the ship, and returning home.

It was even worse when the pilgrims landed at Sherbro. The naked savages shocked them, and they realized for the first time the tremendous effort they would have to put into taming this desolate and wild tropical land.

Jehudi Ashmun, in discussing the situation with Cal, was frankly pessimistic. "It's unfortunate these people should have arrived at the worst possible time, in the middle of the rainy season. But the Colonization Society wouldn't take my advice about sending the first shipload in the spring. I shudder to think what's going to happen when the swamp fever hits. And then there are the savages—they're getting more hostile every day."

"I've talked to Captain Trenchard," Cal told Ashmun. "He's willing to send carpenters ashore to help you build shelters. I only wish we could stay and help too, but our orders are to head down the Gold Coast immediately, after the slavers."

Ashmun clapped his young friend on the shoulder. "I'm grateful for your thoughtfulness. Just promise to come back the first chance you get."

As Cal was leaving the shack Ashmun used as his headquarters a messenger arrived from the *Cyane.* Cal excused himself and opened the envelope that was postmarked Cape Verde.

His face went white.

"What's the matter?" asked Ashmun.

"Oliver caught tropical fever in Trinidad," Cal said hoarsely. "He's dead."

47

He didn't hear Ashmun's condolences, so deep was his grief. The long rivalry between him and Oliver was over, but this wasn't the way he wanted it to end. He couldn't imagine life without Oliver, whom he had loved and admired despite their differences, and now, though the sun shone bright, the day was dark.

4 ⊂⊂⊂⊂⊂⊂⊂⊂⊂⊂⊂⊂⊂

IN THE NEXT MONTHS LIEUTENANT PERRY WAS TO DISCOVER that many of the preconceived ideas he had about slaves and slaveholders were false. He had imagined that the responsibility for the slave trade lay at the door of the southern plantation owner exclusively, and it came as a shock to learn that the African chiefs—who callously supplied the blacks to the traders, and the bankers, insurance men and merchants of many nations who shared in the profitable financial pie—were just as guilty as the southern slaveowner.

The original slaveowners weren't the white traders but the blacks themselves. Sometimes the African chiefs sold their enemies captured in battle to the traders; others who had been branded as criminals by tribal law were condemned to go under the white man's yoke. Often chiefs would declare war on a nearby village merely to get prisoners to sell to the traders, who came to barter their mirrors, cloths and firearms for human flesh. Before the eyes of the first white men fell upon the Gold Coast, slavery had been long established in Africa as an economic system, and the traders bought Negroes who were already slaves. Many Negro slaves in America were better off than their counterparts in Africa.

Still, Cal thought, that was no excuse for the terrible brutality of the white traders, which he saw at first hand.

49

There was one occasion in particular. On a quiet April afternoon in 1820 the *Cyane* came upon a brig on whose main deck there were a suspicious number of Negro women and children. Suddenly they were hurried below, and it was obvious to the Lieutenant that this was a slaver.

"Hoist all sail!" Cal shouted, "Slaver ahead!" As the crew rushed to their stations he put the glass to his eye again. The brig was crowding on sail, trying to get away. It wouldn't. The *Cyane* was much faster than any slave ship loaded down with human cargo.

Cal watched the gap between the two ships diminish. Suddenly he stiffened with horror, unable to believe his eyes. The slaver captain was bringing the blacks up on deck. Crewmen were readying a long, heavy chain. The captain meant to send every slave—man, woman and child—over the side. The murderous devil knew that to be convicted of slave-running, the slaves themselves, not merely their eating utensils, food or manacles, must be found aboard.

Captain Trenchard joined Cal on the bridge. "A bad situation, Lieutenant. The wind's slackening. By the time we catch up with them, it's going to be too late."

"There's one way we might be able to stop it," Cal said. "A lucky shot or two might discourage the monster. Do I have your permission to fire?"

Trenchard frowned. He was an easygoing man who disliked trouble, and what Cal was suggesting was in defiance of the rules. Patrol ships were forbidden to fire upon slavers.

Cal read his thoughts. "But Captain," he said urgently, "if you don't stop them, the entire slave load will be overboard by the time we come within hailing distance. Can you live with the death of two hundred blacks on your conscience?"

The Captain reached a decision. "All right, Lieutenant. Fire away. But remember, if they drown their slaves and we

50

succeed only in damaging the brig or, Heaven forbid, in killing any of the crew, you'll be the one to suffer most in the court of inquiry."

Not bothering to salute, Cal raced from the bridge to the gun deck. There he took over personal command of the battery of eight-pounders, glad now for the long hours of practice he had put in under Oliver and Commodore Rodgers.

When he put the glass to his eye again his blood froze. The crew of the slaver was about to send the first group of blacks over the side.

"Fire!" he shouted, and the eight-pounders belched smoke.

The range was long and three of the balls missed completely, but one was a perfect hit, striking the slaver amidships and killing two of the crew. Cal could see that the crewmen were losing their taste for the job; the captain was having difficulty getting them to approach the panic-stricken Negroes. A knot of crewmen gathered to consult among themselves, but meanwhile the captain, waving a cutlass, succeeded in dragooning a number of others.

"Fire!" Cal shouted again. This time a ball wounded the captain, another crewman, and two of the blacks. To his relief, Cal saw through the glass that the carnage was over. A crewman was running up the flag of surrender.

Trenchard came up, beaming. "Fine shooting, Lieutenant. Fantastic, in fact." His expression changed to one of surprise. "What's the matter? You don't seem so pleased about your victory."

"I'm not, sir. If I'd been a shade more accurate on that second volley, we would have missed the blacks."

The Captain shook his head in wonderment. "Lieutenant, aren't you ever satisfied?"

"I guess not, sir."

"Well, you'll either be dead in ten years or a Commodore

in thirty." He smiled. "Tell me, Lieutenant, do you intend to be a Commodore?"

Cal grinned. "Well, sir, I don't intend to be dead."

The *Cyane* boarded its prize and towed it into port. There the slavers were turned over to the authorities and the blacks set free.

Though in the next months the patrol sloop spent most of its time at sea, taking slave ships and boarding suspicious-looking traders, it stopped often at coastal trading ports to take on fresh provisions and water, and Cal had an opportunity to observe the native chiefs at first hand.

The Africans had many interesting, but also many strange customs. For instance, there was only one way to determine if a native was telling the truth: you had to demand that he "say it with salt fingers," which meant that after eating salt mixed with a pinch of earth, he held two fingers over his head and swore to the truth of what he was saying. For most of the cruise Lieutenant Perry was purchasing officer, and there were many times he was obliged to demand the salt fingers test.

That summer both tropical fever and scurvy broke out aboard the *Cyane*, aided by the long hot rains and Captain Trenchard's disinterest in sanitation. Six men died, and the Lieutenant and his superior officer had many bitter words over the issue.

"Fresh vegetables and cleanliness!" Trenchard scoffed. "How can they prevent disease?"

"I don't know, Captain," Cal said, "but I've observed that they do. If you won't let me fumigate the ship, at least let's turn north to the Canaries for fresh provisions and a cooler climate."

Reluctantly Trenchard agreed. The *Cyane* anchored at the Portuguese port of Teneriffe. When fresh provisions had been stowed aboard, Cal went ashore to arrange with the

Governor for the customary exchange of salutes which international courtesy demanded.

After a half hour's wait in the Governor's anteroom, a tight-lipped young Lieutenant of the U.S. Navy was shown into the Governor's study. To keep a naval officer waiting so long was an insult to the American flag, and after saluting, Cal stated his business briskly.

"Your Excellency, the sloop *Cyane* is leaving Teneriffe immediately. We would appreciate the exchange of a ten-gun salute." He saluted again and turned on his heel to leave.

"One moment, Lieutenant," the Governor said. "I am afraid our salute must be one gun less than yours. The United States, as a republic, cannot be recognized as the equal of a kingdom."

Cal's nostrils flared. "Sir, the United States is the equal of any nation in the world."

"I do not think so, Lieutenant, and in Portuguese territory it is my opinion that counts."

"In that case there will be no exchange of courtesies whatsoever."

The Governor smiled coldly. "If that is what you wish."

"It isn't what I wish, sir," Cal replied. "It's what respect for my country demands."

He returned to the *Cyane*. The sloop weighed anchor and slid from Teneriffe harbor for the return trip to Cape Mesurado, where Trenchard planned to pick up the carpenters he had left to help Jehudi Ashmun and the colonists.

The infant colony was in desperate straits. Against the advice of Ashmun, his white co-administrators of the colony had been persuaded by a dishonest English trader, who stood to profit from their needs, to build their settlement on a swampy island off the coast. The colonists had refused either to work or to build a stockade, knowing they could not fight off attacks by the increasingly hostile savages. Twenty-three of them had died, among them several of the white leaders and one of the bluejacket carpenters.

"There's only one thing to do," Ashmun told Cal. "Start all over again and build the colony not at Sherbro, but further up the coast, near the mouth of the Mesurado River. There's good dry land there. But I have two very big problems. First, to convince my colleagues that we should take another stab at building a colony, and second, to find a surveyor who can choose a good site."

"Maybe I can talk Captain Trenchard into putting in a good word for your plan," Cal told the missionary. "And if you can make do with an amateur surveyor, I think I'll be able to choose a site for you. We have a lot of free time slave-chasing, and I've been studying some books on surveying."

Ashmun looked at his young friend with admiration. "Cal, you're the answer to a missionary's prayer."

Cal badgered Captain Trenchard till he agreed to speak to the colony administrators in behalf of a new location, and meanwhile went out of his way to let Ashmun's colleagues know that Trenchard had great influence with the Navy and State departments, something that wasn't necessarily true. Besieged on all sides, the administrators finally agreed to rebuild the colony elsewhere on the coast if Lieutenant Perry was able to recommend a satisfactory site.

Cal broke out the surveying instruments aboard the *Cyane* and took a longboat and three men to explore the coast near the mouth of the Mesurado River. It took him three days to find a first class site on the river highlands. The land was good for farming, dry and of desirable elevation, and the river afforded an excellent defensive barrier for the stockade Ashmun planned to build.

The colony officials approved the site and, at Jehudi Ash-

54

mun's suggestion, asked Cal to parley with the native chiefs for it.

The palavers taught the young lieutenant a good deal about the delicate art of negotiation. First of all, Cal learned, it was necessary to know as much as possible about the people with whom you were dealing, to collect any and all facts on their customs, prejudices and habits. The Mesurado chiefs didn't belong to an especially intelligent race, but they were a prideful one, and, Ashmun aside, one mistake the colonists had made in dealing with them was to treat the chiefs not as equals, but as naughty children. Cal was careful to show his conferees the respect and consideration that they craved, and as a result they were eager to please him. Nor did he offer for the land site less than he thought it was worth. When the contract was signed, in lamb's blood, as was the local custom, relations between the white colonists and the black chiefs were materially improved.

Cal went home sooner than he had expected. Fever had broken out again on the *Cyane,* and Trenchard headed the sloop back to New York. The ship encountered severe winter storms and strong head winds during its fifty-seven-day voyage, and when it dropped anchor in New York harbor on Christmas Day, 1821, Cal limped off the gangplank and into Jane's arms feeling that he had seen enough of Africa to last him a lifetime.

Against Cal's protests, Jane put him to bed for a complete rest, but after the first day he was demanding writing supplies. When he was supposed to be asleep, Jane would come into the bedroom to find him writing recommendations to the Navy Department on ship sanitation and hygiene.

"Fever and scurvy are *preventable,*" he kept lecturing Jane and even little Matthew junior whenever they would listen. "You can be sure of one thing—my next ship won't have a single case of illness on it."

It was a while before he was able to put his newfangled theories to the test, but six months later he was made acting commander of the sloop-of-war *Shark*, with orders to take Dr. Eli Ayres, the new commissioner of the Liberian colony, to Africa. On the trip to Cape Mesurado he saw to it that every crewman aboard had daily rations of lime juice to prevent scurvy, and when the ship reached tropical waters, he took drastic measures against the fever.

The latter didn't endear him to his men. They not only were forbidden to go ashore at night, but must also steam themselves before the blazing bonfires Captain Perry ordered built on the decks. The men complained to Dr. Ayres, a pompous man filled with his own importance, and Ayres took up their resentments with the Captain.

Cal gave Ayres short shrift. "Doctor," he told him, "I intend to protect these men's lives whether they like it or not."

Ayres mopped his streaming forehead. "But Captain, surely you don't hope to keep off the fever with fire and sweat!"

"It seems to be working," Cal told him.

"But you might just as well beat a tom-tom, like the natives," Ayres protested, and strode away toward the bow, as far away from the roaring bonfire as he could get.

Neither Cal nor Ayres guessed the real reason why Cal's sanitary measures worked: the fire kept off the mosquitoes, whose bites spread the disease.

The *Shark* dropped anchor at Mesurado. Jehudi Ashmun was away on a brief trip up the coast, and Cal heard from the settlers of the terrible trials the new colony had recently suffered and the heroic part Ashmun had played in them.

The natives, though friendly at first, had turned against the colonists, and one day Ashmun learned that an attack was planned on the settlement. He was no soldier, but he had prepared for war like a seasoned campaigner, drilling the

56

twenty-seven men who were well enough to fight, and clearing the ground around his rough stockade. He was the only leader the colony had left; two of his colleagues had died and one had disappeared since Cal's last trip to Liberia.

Ashmun had two brass cannon and a little powder. Collecting what muskets, swords and pikes he had, the missionary had prepared for the savages' attack. The fever struck him down, but in spite of it he had managed to keep control of the panic-stricken settlers. Then one night the jungle echoed with drumming and savage cries, and a friendly native brought word that the colony could expect the blacks to move against it that midnight.

A screaming horde of 900 savages fell on the little stockade. Ashmun waited till the howling blacks were within close range, and then set a match to one of his tiny cannon. As grapeshot mowed down a score of the wild men the black ranks broke, then re-formed to attack. One of Ashmun's men fell with a spear in his throat, then another, and another. Ignoring his losses, Ashmun rammed home another load of grapeshot and touched it off. Every bit of scrap and metal told, and this time the charge was stopped. Yelling with fear, the savages disappeared into the jungle, leaving more than a hundred dead behind.

Of his own forces, Ashmun had four dead and four wounded; he himself had suffered a spear slash in his thigh. But the war was far from over. For three terrible weeks the intrepid missionary and his tiny forces mounted guard night and day. From the jungle came nerve-jangling screams and the insidious beat of tom-toms, and it was plain that the savages were getting up courage for another attack. When it came at dawn Ashmun was ready. He used the same tactics, the cannon taking heavy toll, although this time hand-to-hand fighting was also necessary. The wild men fled into the bush, leaving their spears behind.

When Ashmun returned to the colony a few days later, Cal was able to congratulate him personally. "So you've won," he said. "At long last, and thanks to you, Liberia's finally a reality."

"Thank God, not me," replied Ashmun simply.

The *Shark* now joined the American squadron patrolling the coast in search of slavers, and Cal made several captures, among them a French ship with a cargo of over two hundred slaves. Sailing as far as the West Indies, the *Shark* rounded the Antilles and then turned north toward New York. In mid-January 1822 she berthed in New York harbor, her six-month voyage over.

Tragic news awaited Lieutenant Perry in Newport. His brother Alexander had been drowned in Valparaiso, Chile, going to the rescue of a drowning shipmate. His mother was ill, and fated to die before the end of winter.

Cal didn't have much time to brood. By spring the *Shark* was off again to Vera Cruz, Mexico, where its job, as part of a squadron commanded by Commodore David Porter, was to convoy merchantmen past the coasts of Cuba and Florida. From the islands of the West Indies and the inlets of the Everglades, a new breed of pirates were preying on American shipping. Unlike the pirates of the seventeenth and eighteenth centuries, who often fought against great odds merely for the joy of bloodying a cutlass, these men were more like small-time criminals of the seas. They sailed in schooners of low draft, manned by only five or six men, and attacked a ship only when they were sure of success. They went after unarmed merchantmen, to whose crews and passengers they showed no mercy. When a man-of-war appeared on the horizon they were quick to scuttle away.

Commodore Porter had realized that a battleship was much too cumbersome and unwieldy to deal with such quick, maneuverable antagonists as the pirate fleet, and he had brought with him to Vera Cruz, along with several schooners of the *Shark* class, thirty-odd large sailboats. These boats, equipped with small cannon, would be able to follow the small pirate schooners to their swampy lairs, and their crews could engage the enemy on land in direct hand-to-hand combat.

On the day Commodore Porter posted the crews and commanding officers of the "Mosquito Fleet," as the sailboats were dubbed, Lieutenant Perry was shown into his cabin aboard the squadron flagship.

"Yes, Lieutenant?" Porter had heard of the strapping, 28-year-old officer's exploits off the Gold Coast, and was glad to meet him.

"Sir, I request pro tem command in the Mosquito Fleet, after the squadron has anchored in Florida waters."

Porter's eyebrows rose. "But Lieutenant, I thought I made it perfectly clear that midshipmen were in command of the Mosquito Fleet. Certainly you're not asking for a demotion in rank!"

"No, sir. But the pirates seem to be eluding our war schooners in the coastal areas, at least for the moment, and I'm anxious to see some action."

"Well, this is a highly unusual request. Wouldn't you mind being mixed up with a bunch of lowly midshipmen? And this kind of work isn't going to be very pleasant—the Everglades can get very hot. Not to mention the danger: these pirates give and ask no quarter. I know you're a married man."

"I believe I can stand the middies for a while. I don't mind danger, and as far as the temperature's concerned, I prefer extreme heat to cold."

"Lieutenant," Porter laughed, "I strike my colors!" He consulted the Mosquito Fleet postings. "Lieutenant Marston, as you know, is in charge of the Everglades expedition; though you outrank him, he'll be commanding officer. You'll take over sailboat number nine with a crew of four. I'll appoint Ensign Sangster as temporary acting captain of the *Shark* in your absence from Vera Cruz."

Three days later two of Porter's cruisers, with twenty sailboats in tow, left for the Florida coast. The Gulf weather was mild, and the squadron was intact when it anchored in Big Marco Bay, near the Everglades.

Cal found himself fascinated by the strange, prehistoric swamps with their natural canals and miles of sawgrass-covered plains and sand prairies. No man had ever seen the entire stretch of the Everglades, and it would be a double adventure tracking down the pirates in this land that God seemed to have forgotten.

The strategy of the pirate-hunters was to lurk watchfully in one of the thousands of inlets, and then set off in pursuit of any suspected pirate boat sailing up or down the Gulf. Often the Navy boat would pursue the pirates to their hidden rendezvous.

Sometimes the pirates would see the Navy boats approaching and scuttle back into the swamps before they were seen. Often the pirates, though they fled, would be too strong in number for one or two Navy boats to pursue. Most often the Navy boats would be too far distant from their quarry to have any hope of catching them. The only real purpose the Navy sailboats filled was to allow the merchantmen to proceed on their courses unmolested. This, though it fully satisfied the merchantmen, wasn't to the liking of the adventure-seeking young officers and crewmen.

"Porter didn't send enough boats," Lieutenant Marston grumbled to Cal. "We need more than twenty. We need five hundred."

Cal nodded. He slapped at a mosquito and for the hundredth time that day glanced toward the lookout who was scanning the inshore waters of the Gulf, sitting with spyglass in the top branches of a stunted pine.

In a week of swamp-skulking they set out after six pirate boats, but the closest they came to any of them was half a mile. The luck of the other Navy crews was only slightly better; one followed an enemy boat to its hiding place and destroyed the pirate camp, though the buccaneers managed to escape. The small cannon of another sank a pirate craft at the mouth of an inlet and killed one of its crew, but the rest jumped overboard and vanished into the swamps they knew so well.

"Sailboats ahoy!" shouted the lookout, "two miles south. Two of 'em! They're after a schooner headed up the Gulf toward Porpoise Point."

Eagerly the lounging men left the bank and piled into the waiting sailboats. With Cal taking the tiller of one and Marston that of the other, the two boats caught the breeze and headed out into the Gulf.

This time, Lieutenant Perry was glad to see, they had a chance to catch the marauders. The south by west wind favored the Navy sails and the pirates hadn't yet seen them; if the breeze kept steady they would be able to head off at least one of the pirate craft before it could reach the haven of the shoreline.

The Navy boats swept ahead, Cal's in the lead. He watched the gap between him and the pirate craft diminish. The buccaneers had seen them now and, hoisting all their sail, turned back toward shore.

"Ready, Jones?" Cal asked the gunner.

"Aye, sir."

"We should be within range in a few minutes."

Marston's cannon fired, but the ball fell short. Cal clucked to himself in exasperation. Marston was a good officer, but he should have waited till the range had shortened; there were only three cannon shot aboard each sailboat, and they had to make every ball count. The pirates outnumbered them almost two to one, and cannon were the only weapons the Navy sailboats had to make up for the disadvantage.

Six hundred yards . . . five hundred and fifty. The pirates opened up with musket fire, and a ball struck the water ten yards in front of the sailboat's bow.

"Sir," one of the crewmen said nervously, "kin we return that shootin'? It's gettin' mighty close."

"Not close enough, Randall," Cal answered, and the other men laughed, breaking the tension.

Another musket ball whistled past Cal's head, and he ordered the crew to take cover, hunching himself down at the tiller in order to make as small a target as possible. Another ball struck the boom, and carromed off.

They were close enough now to try a cannon shot, and motioning to one of the men to take the tiller, Cal crawled to the bow.

He ducked as a musket ball splintered the gunwhale near his head.

"Fire away, Jones," Cal told the gunner.

"Aye, sir," Jones said, and lit the fuse.

The cannon boomed, while Cal peered over the gunwhale.

"Good shooting! A one foot hole in the side. They're shipping water badly. Try another ball at the second boat."

Jones' ball missed this time, but a shot from Marston's cannon told, and the sailboats closed in on the enemy with the odds about equal.

At fifty feet Jones' last ball scored a direct hit, sinking one of the pirate boats. "Don't shoot the swimmers!" Cal shouted, as one of his men drew a bead. "We want to take them prisoner! Concentrate your fire on the other boat!"

Cal noticed Marston was having trouble. The pirates' musket fire had wounded several of his men, and his boat was nearly out of control. He would have to take the second pirate boat by himself.

The Navy sailboat moved in closer to its quarry, the men keeping to what cover the shallow gunwhales afforded, firing their muskets at the pirate crew. Cal hoped their marksmanship was good; the buccaneers were better men with cutlasses and knives than his young bluejackets, and the Navy men were sure to get the worst of a hand-to-hand fight.

The pirate fire slackened, and Cal took a quick look at the enemy craft. Yes, his men's bullets had told; there were only three buccaneers still blazing away at them. As he watched one clapped a hand to his side and slipped down into the scuppers.

In another minute they had reached the pirate boat. A bluejacket threw out a grappling hook and Cal got to his feet, cocking his pistols. "We'll take them with pistols and cutlasses, boys!" he yelled, and led the charge over the side.

The two desperadoes still unwounded were dangerous men, and they knew how to fight in close quarters, but Cal cut down one with a vicious swipe of his cutlass and one of the crewmen shot the other, though not before the man had wounded one of the sailboat's crew. Thirty yards away Marston was picking up the survivors of the other pirate craft.

The miniature sea battle had gone well enough. Only three of the bluejackets were superficially wounded and six or seven of the pirates would never swing a cutlass again. Knowing that a pirate always preferred talking to hanging, Cal and Marston had no difficulty getting the survivors to reveal the locations of the hidden camps.

The next morning the two cruisers made the first of several forays up the inlets and canals of the Everglades. They destroyed four camps fairly near the coast, took a number of prisoners, and dispatched punitive expeditions for the sack-

63

ing of other pirate camps deeper in the swamp interior. Within another two weeks the pirate menace of the Florida coast had been destroyed, and the squadron returned to its rendezvous at Vera Cruz, to receive the congratulations of Commodore Porter.

Cal, next assigned to convoy duty off Cuba, was given credit for the single-handed capture of two pirate brigs before Porter detached him from active duty. The *Shark* docked in New York harbor in the summer of 1823, after fifteen of the busiest months in its young commander's career.

He was very glad to get a six-month furlough.

5

THE FURLOUGH WAS FINE, AND SO WAS THE BIRTH OF LITTLE
Oliver Hazard, but the six months stretched into a year and
Lieutenant Perry still hadn't heard from the Navy Department about another command. He was a devoted family man
who loved his wife and children, but the job of a sailor was
to sail, and restlessness was nagging at him. It was a great
relief when he was called to the office of Commodore
Rodgers, told he had been promoted to Lieutenant-Commander, and offered the place of executive officer aboard the
new battleship *North Carolina* under Captain Charles Morgan. Rodgers himself would command the Mediterranean
squadron, with the *North Carolina* as his flagship.

"This is a great honor," said the new Lieutenant-Commander, "and I accept with the greatest pleasure. I know the
North Carolina is the most powerful ship afloat. Would I be
guessing right that she's bound for Port Mahon and her
international debut?"

"Yes, the presence of the Mediterranean squadron at
Minorca, in the West Mediterranean, is mainly for purposes
of diplomacy. Africa and the Levant, the countries bordering
the east shore of the Mediterranean, are pretty quiet just
now; our main job at Mahon and elsewhere in the Medi-

terranean will be to prove that the U.S. Navy can be the equal of the British and the French in the polish of its manners, the brilliance of its uniforms, and the amount of sail it can unfurl."

"Sir, when do you think we'll be under way?" Cal asked. The Mediterranean station at the southern tip of Spain, with its pomp, ceremony and brilliant social life, was every naval officer's dream.

"Not for another six months at least," said Rodgers. "There's a lot of recruiting to be done, Commander, and I want you to take charge of it at all five of our naval stations. The sooner you fill our complements the sooner we'll weigh anchor, and let me tell you this: so far the recruiting's going far from well."

"I don't doubt it. As you know, Commodore, I've written many memorandums to the Department on the subject. We take practically every man or boy who can be talked into enlisting, and it's the worst thing we could do—at least a quarter of every crew falls ill or proves unfit and has to be invalided home at Navy expense."

Cal warmed to his theme. "I don't know why the Navy Secretary won't listen to my recommendations! I've written at least five reports describing a plan whereby boys from all walks of life would be taken on as apprentices and given special training, thus providing a pool from which midshipmen can be drawn. A young boy doesn't belong at sea; he serves for a while and then drifts around the lowest seaports of the world, getting into trouble. And sir," he finished, his voice rising, "do you think it's fair for the Navy to choose only boys from the best families as officer material?"

Smiling, the old sea dog got up from his chair. "Commander, I approve of your ideas and your idealism and hope someday something will be done about them. Meanwhile we've got to limp along as best we can."

Cal's next job after the recruiting was to put the *North Carolina* in shape for her maiden voyage. He didn't get much help from his superior officer, Captain Morgan, who, by tradition, was unapproachable except for the most important decisions. Thus, as executive officer, Cal was responsible for everything else, and that meant being on duty day and night for the thousand and one small problems that came up constantly. He was weary and overworked, and yet he got a tremendous thrill when he came on deck in the morning and saw the mountain of canvas over the jet-black hull, the three tiers of one hundred and two guns, the fresh paint and polished brasswork and Old Glory fluttering astern. This was his ship and he felt proud to be its second in command. To be executive officer of a battleship, after sixteen years in the Navy, was no mean achievement.

The *North Carolina* sailed from New York harbor in April, 1825, and joined the Mediterranean squadron at Tangier. Sailing eastward, the squadron touched at Algiers, Tripoli, then Tunis, where the Lieutenant-Commander received word of the birth of his twin daughters Jane and Caroline. In the Moslem ports Rodgers and his men were welcomed with much flattering ceremony. Now that the American Navy was beginning to rank with the British, the Bey of Algiers had decided to sign a treaty with the United States giving it the same trading rights enjoyed by the English.

At the eastern end of the Mediterranean, Rodgers' squadron found more important work to occupy it—the protection of American shipping. The Greeks had rebelled against the Turks, and the pirates of the Levant were taking advantage of the resulting disorder to prey upon the ships of all nations. Two of Rodgers' ships, the *Macedonian* and the *Erie,* fought off pirates when they tried to attack American merchant ships doing business with the ports of Athens and Corinth.

The *North Carolina* docked at Patras on the Greek coast.

One afternoon Lieutenant-Commander Perry was having lunch in his cabin when he heard loud voices from shore. He looked out of the porthole to see seven veiled women being prodded up the gangplank by two Greek soldiers. A crowd of Moslems laughed and gesticulated below.

Visitors were allowed on the flagship, but this unusual procession looked like trouble. The Commander put down his napkin and went out on deck.

"What's going on here?" he asked the guard.

"Sir, these Greeks want us to buy these Moslem women as slaves. They say they'll sell them very cheap." He hid a grin.

The Commander was half amused and half angry. The women were undoubtedly the widows of Turks killed in revenge by the Greeks for the Turks' sacking of Corinth. Out of Corinth's 100,000 population, less than two thousand Greeks had survived the terrible Turkish atrocities.

"Ask them to wait," he told the surprised guard, and went to Commodore Rodgers' quarters.

"Sir," he asked the Commodore, "why don't we ransom these poor women by taking up a collection among the men? They must have families on the coast, perhaps in Smyrna."

Rodgers smiled. "I doubt if Jane would fancy you with a harem. But go ahead with your collection."

The crew of the *Carolina* was sympathetic to the plight of the Moslem women, and they were purchased from their captors. Cal was embarrassed when the women tried to show their gratitude by kissing the very deck he walked on, and he was glad when the ship reached Smyrna and the refugees were disembarked.

His errand of mercy had unfortunate consequences. The second night in Smyrna a fire that threatened the water front broke out in town. Dressed in oilskins, Commander Perry, led the flagship contingent that went ashore to help fight it.

Drenched with water and chilled with cold, he was one

of the last to return to the *Carolina,* and the doctor immediately put him to bed. A soaring temperature and aching muscles kept him there for more than a week, and for the rest of his life, he suffered from spells of extremely painful rheumatism. As a result of this chronic affliction he gained a reputation for irritability and bad temper that was completely undeserved.

Rodgers' fleet cruised westward, and stopped at Trieste, where the Emperor of Austria and his party came aboard. A page, dressed magnificently in gold and green, leaned against what he thought was a solid mast. The windsail gave way and the page lost his footing, spun a short distance down the deck to a hatchway, and tumbled through it.

One of the crewman came dashing up to Cal, who was conversing with his imperial visitor on the quarter-deck.

"Sir," he panted, "I'm sorry to disturb you, but the Emperor has fallen down the hatch!"

Commander Perry saved the situation by saying to his Majesty: "You see, your Highness, in our democracy we have such respect for royalty that every man of your party is at least an Emperor!"

In Gibraltar, which the squadron reached in October, 1826, the Commander learned he had been appointed to the grade of acting Master Commandant, with a Captaincy only one step away. Commodore Rodgers had written his superiors in Washington that "Commander Perry is the finest executive officer who has ever served under me, and I predict for him the highest achievements."

When Rodgers showed the Commander a copy of the letter the latter's reaction was typical—he smiled and frowned in quick succession and said, "Sir, I hope I'm worthy of your trust."

The fleet dropped anchor in Port Mahon, near Gibraltar, for refitting and supplies. Port Mahon was a glamorous place.

Whitewashed houses straggled up the hill; red-legged partridges strutted everywhere, and there were exotic eating places where one could dine royally on the famous local date-fish for the price of a few coppers. The Commandant and his men would have enjoyed it more had not the weather turned cold and rainy. Colds and catarrh laid the squadron low. Smallpox followed and the sick bay was jammed with a hundred and twenty-five men.

The fleet set sail for Malta, where the authorities placed it under quarantine and sent smallpox vaccine aboard. Cal, with his constant fumigating and scrubbing and dosing, was an unpopular officer with the men. A delegation of crewmen went so far as to complain to the doctor, claiming that the Commandant's cure was worse than the disease. The doctor took their complaint to Commodore Rodgers.

Rodgers heard him out, then replied, "Doctor, the Commandant's notions on shipboard sanitation and hygiene may be newfangled, but I have the greatest confidence in them and in him. I suggest that the men cultivate a little of the same."

It wasn't till spring, 1827, that the smallpox epidemic was completely eradicated. On May 31 the bos'n sounded the call, "All hands up anchor for home!" No man in the fleet was gladder to hear it than Commandant Perry, though there was bad news waiting for him at home—Raymond had died at Bristol, Rhode Island, while on shore duty.

When, one day in 1829, the maid brought the official Navy Department letter to the breakfast nook and set it down before her employer, Commandant Perry looked at the envelope and then propped it up against the marmalade jar.

Jane sucked in her breath. "Cal! Aren't you going to open it?"

He shook his head. "Not this very minute. I've been waiting at home twenty months for that letter, and even if the Department bigwigs can't see me doing it, I'm going to take my time." He smiled at his wife. "How long do you think I'll be away this time? And where do you think they're sending me? Africa? The Caribbean? The North Pole?"

Jane was in a fever of impatience to know the answers to these questions herself, and she couldn't bear to play along with her husband's little game. She rapped him sharply across the knuckles. "Cal, if you don't open that letter this minute, then *I* will!"

"A man must obey his superior officer." Cal smiled and reached for the letter. Deliberately tearing the envelope down the side, he took out the sheet of folded paper. He read it once, then reread it, while Jane impatiently tapped the table.

"I've been placed in command of the new sloop-of-war *Concord,* seven hundred tons and nineteen guns. By orders of President Jackson I'm to convey John Randolph of Virginia on a diplomatic mission to Kronstadt, the port of Saint Petersburg, Russia."

"Russia!" Jane was horrified.

"Who knows, maybe I'll have a chance to meet the Tsar!"

"But Cal, it's so far away, and you'll be gone for ages!"

"The Navy Secretary doesn't mention how long the trip will be. But I'll tell you one, thing, Jane—even if the trip's dull as haddock, it will be my first official command, and I'll have a chance to put some of my training ideas into action. My first request, when I apply for officers to man the *Concord,* will be for a chaplain who can teach my midshipmen history, literature and mathematics while they're learning seamanship. Any man of mine who has a special talent is going to be given the opportunity to develop it."

Jane sighed. "Well, I've had you to myself for almost two

71

years now. I guess I shouldn't complain, though your sister certainly will—you haven't seen her since last Christmas."

"My dear, I'll bring you back the biggest, fiercest Russian bear I can find, and give her cubs to sister Jane."

"Don't you dare!" Jane shrieked, so loudly that Matthew and little Oliver Hazard, the former running and the latter crawling, came into the room. Cal was forced to promise he would bring home from Russia as many presents as the *Concord* could safely stow in her hold.

The *Concord* set sail from New York in mid-June, and stopped off in Norfolk, Virginia, to take aboard its distinguished passenger, Senator John Randolph. Its next destination was Kronstadt, forty-three sailing days away.

It was a rough voyage of storms and gales, and Randolph, now a senile and crochety old man, made it even more difficult for Captain Perry and his crew. Because a rolling deck made him lose his footing and his dignity, the Senator hated the sea, and he disliked Captain Perry because he refused to agree that, as an Ambassador of the State Department, Randolph outranked him in the *Concord's* command. The Captain was careful to protect his crew from Randolph's orders, and there was scarcely a day that the Senator, furious at some new slight, didn't come knocking at his cabin door for an explanation or an apology, which the Captain had no intention of giving.

The conflict between the two men came to a head when Randolph witnessed the flogging of a crewman who had broken into the ship's stores and stolen some grog. The use of the "cat" for certain offenses was the rule of the service, and had been a part of Navy discipline since before Cal was born. The Senator from Virginia couldn't understand that, and his humanitarian principles were outraged. He observed the punishment with loathing, and when it was over came and knocked violently on the Captain's door.

"Sir!" the old man shouted, "I shall report you to the State Department when my mission is done. You are a brute, sir! I treat my own slaves better than you treat your crewmen. Never once has a slave been flogged on the Randolph plantation!"

"Unless I am mistaken, Senator," Captain Perry said coolly, "this is not your plantation, but the sloop-of-war *Concord*, of the United States Navy."

"That's no excuse!" stormed Randolph.

The Captain tried to reason with the Senator, though he felt it was really useless. "Mr. Randolph," he said evenly, "if you were to examine the log of the *Concord* and the logs of every other ship in which I ever held command, you would find that not more but less than the average of stripes was administered. I'm more anxious to use an ounce of prevention than a pound of cure. The real reason why seamen get into so much trouble is that they drink too much ardent spirits. I've done my best to have liquor ration abolished for minors, and if possible, for adult seamen too."

The Senator sneered. "I do not accept your excuses. And I do not believe a court martial will either. Good day, Captain. Your messman may serve my dinner in my cabin."

The Captain had become friendly with Alfred Jenks, the ship's Chaplain, and he confided his worries about Randolph to him. "I know the man's going to make trouble, Alfred. And he has a lot of influence at home."

"I wouldn't be too concerned," the Chaplain said. "Not when you know your officers would take your side hands down, if any real kind of controversy develops."

The *Concord* arrived at Kronstadt on August 9. It was Randolph's mission to reach an agreement with the Russian authorities on fishing rights in the Bering Straits, and Captain Perry was glad to see him off the ship, if only for the moment. Tsar Nicholas was in Kronstadt at the time, and he

73

honored the *Concord* with an inspection, later inviting the Captain and Chaplain Jenks to a more informal visit at the palace in St. Petersburg.

The Captain and the Tsar had much in common. They were both big men of a commanding manner, and about the same age, in their middle thirties. Both were lovers of the sea. With Chaplain Jenks acting as interpreter they had already discussed naval matters with the greatest mutual interest and pleasure. Now, in the magnificent palace filled with armor, priceless tapestries and trophies of old wars, the Tsar resumed the conversation.

"I have heard," he said, "of the advances you have been making with the steamboats that ply your magnificent rivers. What has your Navy done to apply steam to your warships"

"Your Majesty," the Captain replied, "you've hit upon a subject close to my heart. For some time other naval officers and myself have been trying to interest the Department in steam warships, but the tradition-bound men of the old line Navy have only scoffed at us. Either they think it's treasonable to suggest that the glorious old wooden sailing ships be replaced by steel monsters who belch dirty smoke, or they don't believe steam can be effectively applied to a large man-of-war. They say that the steamboat, after all, is still in its infancy."

Nicholas nodded, and sighed. "Yes, there are always those who would interfere with progress. Fortunately there are also men like ourselves, who revere the past, but do not necessarily believe that the future must be inferior to it."

Over three kinds of vodka, one with buffalo grass at the bottom of the bottle, the two men discussed naval matters for quite some time, and then the Tsar turned to Chaplain Jenks, and asked him several questions about American education. The Emperor was well-informed on the latest teaching methods, as the Captain could tell from the admiration on Jenks' face, though Cal didn't understand a single word they were saying.

The Captain's attention must have been wandering, for the next thing he knew, a flustered Jenks was saying something so preposterous to him that he couldn't believe his ears.

"Did I hear you right?" he asked the Chaplain.

"His Majesty," Jenks said, swallowing hard, "says that the two of us must stay on in Russia, you to take command of the Russian Navy, I to administer state education."

The Captain looked at the Tsar. Jenks wasn't babbling; the look in the Emperor's eyes could only be described as determined. Nicholas was a man accustomed to getting what he wanted. How was a simple sailor to get out of this particular quandary?

"Tell his Majesty," said Captain Perry, "that we would accept with pleasure, if our government would only allow us to. But we've signed Navy articles for twenty years"—he tried not to grin at the white lie—"and there's no way of getting out of them. If his Majesty still wants us in twenty years time, we'd be delighted."

Jenks translated, and the Tsar nodded regretfully. "His Majesty says," Jenks reported, "that he understands we are men of honor, and must meet our obligations."

But neither Captain nor Chaplain felt really safe till their carriage had brought them through the narrow, cobbled streets back to the quay and the *Concord*.

6 ⊂⊂⊂⊂⊂⊂⊂⊂⊂⊂⊂⊂⊂

THE *Concord* LEFT RUSSIA FOR THE MEDITERRANEAN, STOPPING at Cowes, on the Isle of Wight, to disembark John Randolph, who planned to go on by train to London. The Captain felt it wasn't the last he had heard of the southerner. He was right; from Copenhagen Randolph wrote a letter to the State Department accusing Captain Perry of more crimes than he could have committed in two lifetimes. Fortunately the State Department knew what John Randolph was like, and after a brief investigation, let the matter drop.

For the next nine months the *Concord* cruised the Mediterranean, guarding American shipping from the pirates of the Levant. In Tunis, where he was the guest of the Bey, Captain Perry became friendly with his daughter, the Princess Kamou. The Princess was something of an oddity, a Moslem girl who wanted to study medicine at a time when a woman doctor was not only unknown in the Arab world, but when the very idea of a Moslem female physician would have been considered an affront to Allah. After years of argument Kamou had gotten her father's reluctant consent to pursue a medical career, but her future still seemed dim, since medical schools were unknown on the Barbary Coast and no woman student was acceptable at the universities of Europe.

76

Captain Perry got the Princess off in a corner and conversed with her in whispers. "A German medical education is the best in the world," he told her, "and there is no finer school of medicine than Heidelberg. Why not go there, my dear? Some of my friends in America should be able to arrange it for you."

The Princess looked at him in amazement. "But Captain, I'm a *woman!* And there are only men at Heidelberg."

"Quite so," Captain Perry agreed. "But what's to prevent you from dressing in trousers and passing yourself off as a man? If you want to become a doctor badly enough, you'll do it."

Six months later a student from America by the name of Everett Cummings appeared on the campus of Heidelberg. Apart from a rather girlish appearance, he was no different from other students who had come to Heidelberg from around the world. Everett Cummings matriculated for four full years at the ancient institution of male instruction, and graduated with honors in 1835. His career thereafter was even more spectacular. Shedding his masculine attire, he opened an office in Philadelphia as Madame Kamou, the only woman doctor in the city. In the Civil War Madame Kamou became famous as a nurse. The Tunisian Princess never forgot the debt she owed Matthew Calbraith Perry as the man whose imaginative suggestion had started her on her useful career.

The *Concord* anchored at Port Mahon in June, 1832. In July several men-of-war arrived under the command of Commodore John Patterson, who had a special assignment in Mediterranean waters. He explained it to Captain Perry over a glass of port.

"From eighteen-o-nine to eighteen-twelve, the Neapolitan government under Joseph Bonaparte, Napoleon's brother, confiscated numerous American ships and cargoes. The claims filed against Naples amount to almost two million dollars. After the Bonapartes were overthrown, these claims were repudiated by the present Bomba, who rules Naples as its King. Until recently we were in no position to collect the monies due, but now President Jackson is determined to see justice done. He has sent the Honorable John Nelson as special envoy to King Bomba, and Nelson is at the court of Naples now. Since he hasn't been successful, stronger measures are called for. I'm to take most of the Mediterranean fleet, divided into two units, and sail into Naples harbor. We'll see if American ships, with their guns pointed at the city, don't change the King's mind."

Captain Perry nodded with interest. Things had been pretty dull in Port Mahon recently, and he would welcome a little excitement. "Sir," he said, "I assume the *Concord* will be one of the men-of-war chosen to teach the King a lesson?"

"Yes, but under the command of another officer."

The Captain's face fell, and Patterson was quick to reassure him. "I want you to command the first of two squadrons that will be sailing into Naples harbor. After a few days, I'll be along with the second. Can you be ready to leave with the first contingent tomorrow morning?"

"Sir, I'm not at all well-prepared for this kind of diplomacy. I have only one dress uniform to my name, and that's badly in need of a cleaning."

Patterson frowned. "We'll undoubtedly be making a lot of calls at court. The only solution is to outfit you with new uniforms when we arrive in Naples. But there's one consolation—the Neapolitans are among the best tailors in the world."

The 54-gun flagship *Brandywine*, Captain Perry in temporary command, along with six other ships of the Mediterranean fleet, anchored in Naples harbor two days later. The Captain was obliged to wait three days before Naples tailors

78

made up the proper uniforms, and then he and John Nelson called on the King. However, even the presence of the imposing naval officer in his magnificent dress blues failed to induce King Bomba to part with his money. As the Captain wrote to Jane, "You have never seen your husband so gorgeous and so forbidding, and yet I might have been a peacock in full plumage for all the effect it had upon his Majesty the King, who is a fat little man with smallish, mean eyes."

A few days later the 47-gun *United States*, Commodore Patterson commanding, led five more ships into Naples harbor, among them the *Concord*. Now there were thirteen United States men-of-war with their guns trained on the city, and the Commodore, the Captain and the envoy went ashore again to call on the King. King Bomba seemed a little nervous, but he still declined to pay his debt.

The next morning the *John Adams* entered port. King Bomba courteously returned its 40-gun salute, but told John Nelson he was too indisposed to hold another meeting. That afternoon the Americans noticed that the harbor defenses had been reinforced with several new cannon, and that troops were drilling in the courtyard of the castle.

At noon of the following day the *Boston* dropped anchor in Naples harbor. Nelson, Patterson and Perry called for a conference with the King. It was the last discussion that was needed; the King agreed to satisfy his American creditors. But as Captain Perry was often to remember, it took four years for Congress to reimburse him for the $246 he paid his Neapolitan tailor out of his own pocket.

Captain Perry rejoined his ship, and the *Concord* left Naples harbor on October 15. It dropped anchor at Portsmouth two months later, and Jane and the children were on the dock to meet a husband and father who had been away from home for thirty months. In this time Captain Perry had sailed twenty-eight thousand miles, been three hundred and forty-five days at sea, and visited nine countries.

Cal Perry had changed since Jane had seen him last. He was a little heavier, a little sterner in manner. But if their Captain had changed, so had the men of the *Concord*. They had read books, visited historical sites in foreign cities, studied many subjects under the able tutelage of chaplain-teachers. They had listened to Captain Perry's talks on how to avoid debt, and they had listened well. Many of them had come to believe in their Captain's own ideal of what a Navy officer should be—not just a creature of professional routine with no interests outside of his own specialized job, but a man of culture, who could hold his own in any discussion of books and ideas. Chaplain Jenks, with his commanding officer's full cooperation, had done his work superlatively well.

In December Commandant Perry applied for command of the New York Navy Yard in Brooklyn, and received it. His fellow officers were surprised that he had made such a request; life at the Navy yard was dull, a matter of routine work and training, and it was likely that Cal Perry would be there for years. As distinguished a naval officer as Perry could surely serve his country better and gain promotion more quickly at sea.

But Calbraith Perry had made his decision, and it was based on a good deal of serious thinking about which his naval friends knew little or nothing. Not only did he want to be at home to see his children grow up, but there was a war on in the Navy Department, and he wanted to be on hand to lend his good right arm to the deserving cause.

"Oh, it's not a shooting war," he told his wife. "It's a private war, fought in offices and drawing rooms between the old mossbacks and the young officers. The mossbacks want things to stay the same; sail was good enough for them, they say;

why do the young whippersnappers keep talking about this newfangled steam? Would a real Navy man ever set foot on the deck of a ship whose engines were controlled by a mechanic? And then there's the matter of new training methods. The old methods are good enough for the old sea dogs, and their only interest in a midshipman is that he know what a yardarm is, and can tell port from stern. Nor do they care that the Europeans are developing new guns and ammunition that can blow the conventional man-of-war out of the water with a single broadside."

"But isn't that always the case, Cal?" Jane said. "Don't the old men always want to hold back progress? And aren't they powerful enough to do it? Don't they always have on their side the public, which doesn't know or care about such things, and the politicians, who want to keep things comfortably as they are?"

The Commandant laughed. "Jane, you've got a lot of questions there. But I can tell you this—if the young men stick together, and fight for the chance to build a new Navy that's in step with the times, they'll win out against the sea dogs. Especially if they can swing enough men like me over to their side."

"So you're throwing in your lot with the rebels?"

"Yes, I am. And it's going to be an exciting revolution. If we succeed in renovating the Navy, that renovation's going to proceed on shore, and I can fight a lot better for it at the Navy yard than at sea, patrolling the Caribbean or holding dress reviews at Port Mahon."

Jane kissed him. "Well, I'm glad, and not just because we're going to be a family again."

On the seventh of January, 1833, Commandant Perry took over the command of the New York Navy Yard. Thereafter he commuted daily to the yard from his new Tarrytown estate by ferryboat across the East River. There were many

81

nights when he was late for dinner, and many, having missed the last boat, when he didn't come home at all. He had a number of ideas he wanted to put to work immediately, and there didn't seem to be enough hours in the day to devote to both these and the routine management of the yard. Yet he still found time, every Sunday, to entertain his own and the neighbors' children on the Perry lawn. The Commandant was known for his egg-and-spoon races, for which both winners and losers got large prizes of candy. The author, Washington Irving, a neighbor of the Perrys, complained good-humoredly about these, saying, "Calbraith, you've ruined my children's appetites and my temper, too."

Within a month or two, several of Commandant Perry's pet projects were under way. One was the formation of a naval library, another the establishment of a naval museum, called the Lyceum, whose purpose was "to promote the diffusion of useful knowledge, to foster a spirit of harmony and a community of interest in the service, and to cement the links which unite us as professional brethren."

Every Navy officer was eligible for membership in the Lyceum, and its lounge became a favorite meeting place for both the Navy yard staff and for officers just returning from a cruise. Many Navy men of scientific bent began dropping into the lounge to discuss and exchange ideas with fellow officers of similar interests. Later the *Naval Magazine*, a well-edited bi-monthly, began its publication from Lyceum headquarters. Few of its issues failed to contain an article urging the establishment of a naval academy, at the time considered a radical idea.

One night at the Lyceum the Commandant got involved in an argument which almost had unpleasant results for him. He was entertaining Commodore Sherman, highest ranking officer on the naval staff and an old sea dog who was strongly opposed to the experiments in steam the Commandant and his group were urging.

When Sherman gave a long and ill-considered judgment on the impractability of converting the service from sail to steam, the Commandant exploded in anger.

"Sir, may I remind you that the British have already produced a steam launch and the French a steam ferry? Are we any less practical than these nations, with whom we have been at war in the past? The past, sir, should be buried when its dead. Commodore, I beg leave to tell you that we are now in the present and that it's the future that lies ahead!"

The junior officers looked at one another in the shocked silence; not even the Captain of the Navy yard spoke this way to a Commodore, especially in public.

Sherman's face was red. "Perry," he snapped, "if your brother Oliver Hazard were sitting here instead of you, I'm sure we would be hearing a different set of opinions."

The Commandant bit his lip. "Sir, doesn't that prove my point? Oliver Hazard happens to be dead. And what we need today is not dead heroes but living, vigorous men who realize that you can't hold back progress no matter how hard certain people try to."

Commodore Sherman got to his feet and stalked to the door, leaving his second glass of port untasted. His two aides followed him out with set faces.

"Sir," one of the Commandant's officers told him, "I fear we won't be celebrating your Captaincy for a while, at least not in the year eighteen thirty-three."

Commandant Perry grinned. "Lieutenant Hastings, that little broadside I just fired was worth it."

But he had more friends in high places than he knew; later that year he was promoted to Captain. His new rank gave him added ammunition in his fight with the old conservatives to modernize the service, and though the battle was far from won, there were signs that the young innovators were gaining ground. The Navy Department took official recognition of the new guns and ammunition being manufactured in Europe, and Captain Perry got permission to run a series of experiments with the new armaments designed to teach Navy gunners the new scientific method of heavy-gun bombardment.

The experiments the Captain now arranged for at Sandy Hook were significant in more ways than one. In giving him permission to conduct them, the old sea dogs were admitting that should the experiments succeed, the days of the old wooden ships were over. Up till now wooden ships of the line had rarely been sunk in battle, even when hammered at for hours and reduced to smoking hulks. Now if the new shells and bombs proved that the best British oak or Indian teak were unable to stand up against them, then the old three deckers would have to go, and frigates would become lower and narrower with fewer and heavier guns. And if even the new wooden ships were defenseless against heavy gunfire, then—Heaven help us!—iron would replace wood and sails would make way for steam.

At Sandy Hook the Captain tested both shells and hollow shot—round projectiles with low velocity and smashing power. Platforms, targets and storage sheds for ammunition and fuses were built on the sandy wastes, and butts were set up at various distances. For a week the air rang with the roar of guns, the new Paixhans and other heavy caliber cannon.

On the last day of the tests a frigate was towed in near shore and anchored there. The Captain gave the command for the hollow shot to be fired at distances ranging from far to near. Then he and his officers boarded the ship to determine the damage.

A senior gunnery officer shook his head. "Sir," he addressed his superior, "even at fifty yards the hollow shot, though it would prove fairly lethal against an exposed crew, affects the ship itself very little."

The Captain nodded. "Think how easily an armored wooden ship would repel hollow shot—like peas off a rhino's hide."

"Do you want the gunners to continue with the shot experiments?" asked the gunnery officer.

"No," replied the Captain. "Begin shelling at the same ranges."

The Captain watched through his glass as the battery of high-powered Paixhans began to shell the frigate at far range. Gradually, as the bombardment continued at closer ranges, his tense face relaxed; the shells were doing heavy damage—smashing through the wooden hull, felling the masts, shattering the forecastle deck.

When the last Paixhan had fired its last round at close range, the Captain turned to his grinning staff.

"Gentlemen, we have proven that the warship of the future will be an armored frigate run by steam. Only an armored steam vessel could have any hope of withstanding such devastating firepower. The old sea dogs at the Navy Department will sigh and grumble, but the writing on the wall is clear. It won't be long before they ask us to carry on Robert Fulton's work and begin the building of another steam man-of-war."

That night there was a family celebration at the Perry home in Tarrytown. Two young naval officers bearing the Perry name took part in the festivities—Matthew junior and young Oliver Hazard, both midshipmen.

The Captain told his young listeners of the *Fulton 1st*, the "steam battery" built for the protection of New York harbor in 1814, and how he had watched one of its trial runs. It had gone five miles an hour, slower than a horse could trot and much slower than a square-rigged man-of-war could sail, but the *Fulton 1st* had nonetheless proven that a heavily armored warship could be powered by steam.

Matthew junior winked at young Oliver. "Father," he said innocently, "can you tell us the dimensions and tonnage of the *Fulton First?*" The Captain's memory for detail was justly famed not only among his officers but among his family, but Matthew was pretty sure his father couldn't remember much about a ship that had been built almost twenty years ago.

The Captain shut his eyes for a moment, concentrating. Then he opened them and said, "She was a hundred and fifty-six feet long, twenty feet wide, and fifty-six feet deep. She had a tonnage of two thousand four hundred and seventy-five. She had masts for sails, and her smokestack was between her foremast and mizzenmast. There were paddle wheels at her stern. For armament she had a deck battery and submarine guns."

"How many submarine guns?" asked the irrepressible Matthew, and Captain Perry laughed, picked up a pillow, and threw it at him.

"Go on," Oliver Hazard. "What happened after the *Fulton First?*"

"In the years following, Ol," his father told him, "there were many minor experiments in the United States, and all of them failed. Fulton was dead, and no one else had his genius. But many naval officers, myself among them, had faith that a steam warship could be built which was capable of cruising for a whole day and attaining a speed of as much as ten miles an hour."

Both boys whistled at the thought of such an achievement, and Matthew said, "Isn't it going to be a tremendous job, building your war steamer? And even if you do build it, what kind of crew are you going to get? The Navy Department isn't going to let you hire engineers who'll be running the ship over the head of the Captain. That's a state of affairs the old diehards won't allow for a moment."

The Captain eyed his son proudly; Matthew was an intelligent boy with an inquiring mind. "Quite true," he answered him. "We'll have to work out a system whereby non-Navy men will be hired to run the engines, till we've trained enough officers to be engineering experts. The new *Fulton Two* is going to be a real challenge."

Calbraith Perry hadn't underestimated the magnitude of the task that lay ahead. For two years Navy men and marine engineers worked under his direction on the *Fulton II*, and many were the frustrations and discouragements that beset them. Despite Navy Department opposition on the ground of "tradition-breaking," the Captain solved the problem of engineering personnel by forming an auxiliary branch of the service which wore special uniforms, received special pay, and were under special regulations. But there was still the matter of building a heavy armored ship which would sail under steam.

Once a boiler burst, injuring an apprentice, and Captain Perry himself went into the steaming engine room to drag him out to safety. He was badly burned on the arm, and needed a doctor's attention. Another time a smokestack, being lifted into place by a crane, fell twenty feet through the air and crushed a section of the scaffolding, missing the Captain by less than a foot.

One of the officers hurried to the Captain's side. "Sir," he shouted anxiously in his ear, "are you all right?"

The Captain smiled at him. "Lieutenant Templeton, it's you who seem a little the worse for wear. I suggest you retire to the Lyceum for a glass of brandy. I give you permission to drink to my health."

By January, 1838, the Fulton *II* was ready for inspection

by Navy Department bigwigs. Designed as a floating battery for the defense of New York harbor, she was certainly that. Her hull was made of the best live oak, with heavy bulwarks five feet thick, beveled on the outside so as to cause an enemy's shot to glance off harmlessly. She had three masts, was 180 feet long and had four huge smokestacks. Her boilers were made of copper, and the paddlewheels had enormous buckets which were almost 23 feet across. Her armament consisted of eight 42-pounders, and one 24-pounder. Her total cost was close to $300,000. In her lockers she carried enough coal for three days of sailing.

"In less than an hour after orders are received," the Captain reported triumphantly to the Navy Department, "the *Fulton II* can be moved in any direction at the rate of *ten miles an hour!*"

To which Washington replied: "Schedule trial coastal cruise as soon as possible."

The old sea dogs were up to their sly tricks. The Captain pointed out that his orders had been to build a floating fortress for harbor defense, not a cruiser. The *Fulton II*, adapted for bays and harbors, was unlikely to prove seaworthy; and besides, her coal bunkers held only a three-day supply of fuel. The Captain knew that if the *Fulton II* failed in a coastal cruise for which she was unequipped, public reaction would delay the development of a steam Navy for at least a decade.

But the Navy Department was adamant, and in late January the *Fulton II* steamed down to Sandy Hook from New York harbor. She had hardly anchored for the night when a storm came up, and in the buffeting she suffered, several of her wheel buckets were badly damaged. She had to limp home for repairs, and the old sea dogs were delighted. But the steamer's failure was only a partial one, and Captain

Perry received permission to take his ship out again in more clement weather.

This time the *Fulton II* passed the test with flying colors. It cruised from Long Island to New London, Connecticut, and back, and though there were heavy head winds, she averaged a speed of seven miles an hour. Not a wheel bucket was broken, and the boilers worked perfectly, though it was necessary for a midshipman to be in constant attendance upon them with a can of hot lead for the sealing of leaks.

There was another celebration at the Tarrytown house. The Captain announced that as soon as the weather turned warmer he was going to take his ship to Washington and show her to President Van Buren and the cabinet.

On May 12, 1838, as bands played and bunting flew, the *Fulton II* chugged up the Potomac and docked at the Presidential wharf. Martin Van Buren and the Secretary of the Navy, J. K. Paulding, congratulated Captain Perry on his successful cruise.

Paulding, a man of romantic temperament who loved the old square-rigged ships, asked the Captain how his men could stand the dirt and heat of the boiler room.

"Mr. Secretary," Captain Perry replied, "you are forgetting the cold deck crews suffer in the teeth of a gale, and the icicles that form in their whiskers."

The President smiled as Paulding wiped soot off his face from the *Fulton II*'s smokestacks. "I daresay, Mister Secretary," he said, "that if an enemy were attacking Washington at this moment, you would rather have grime on your cheek from our defending steam warships, than a splinter of shell in your heart from the warships of the enemy."

Paulding, a prominent author, was at a loss for words.

That August the *Fulton II*, while making its way through the heavy traffic of New York harbor, collided with a brig and stove in the lighter ship's port side. The acting master,

Lieutenant Pickering, hurried to the Navy yard with his heart in his mouth, and blurted out the details of the disaster to his commanding officer.

"I'm sorry, sir," Pickering finished lamely, "it will never happen again," and waited with bowed head for the tongue-lashing he expected to receive from Perry.

But Captain Perry smiled. "You say the *Fulton Two* wasn't harmed in the slightest, Lieutenant?"

"No, sir, but the brig was practically demolished."

"Congratulations, Pickering. You've discovered the battering ram, a principle not used in naval warfare since the old Roman triremes. From now on the ironclad prow of the steam warship will be an offensive weapon. Good work, Lieutenant, and let's make a few more of the same kind of mistakes!"

The steam frigate had definitely proven itself, and in 1839 construction at the Philadelphia Navy Yard was begun on two steamships-of-war, the *Mississippi* and the *Missouri*. The *Mississippi* was 225 feet long and had a crew of 525 men. From her gunbays protruded two 10-inch and eight 8-inch guns, a tremendous amount of firepower. In the 1840's these ships were among the most advanced steam frigates in the world.

And the Navy had Captain Matthew C. Perry to thank for it. When the *Mississippi* and the *Missouri* were completed in 1841, he gained a new title among his fellow officers of the service—"Father of the Steam Navy."

For a man who was reported by those who only knew him superficially to be both stern and humorless, the Captain's joking remark, when he first heard of his new title, was typical. He said, "I don't know if I like it. It sounds like an awful lot of hot air."

7 ᴄᴄᴄᴄᴄᴄᴄᴄᴄᴄᴄ

HE WAS SHORTLY TO RECEIVE ANOTHER TITLE—COMMODORE.
After thirty years of hard work and dedication Calbraith
Perry had reached the topmost rung of Navy command, and
was entitled to the use of the admiral's flag, the broad pennant, both afloat and ashore.

In the fourth decade of the nineteenth century those few
men who could display the broad pennant were a kind of
seagoing king. When a Commodore appeared on the deck
of a ship, that ship was, until he left it, the center of the
naval world. When he dined, he dined alone in his luxurious
cabin, in a dazzle of white napery and cut glass, unless he
deigned to invite a lowly Master Commandant or Captain
to join him.

It was a great, yes, a tremendous satisfaction to have risen
to the top of his chosen profession, to have drawn even with
Oliver, at least. And yet the Commodore felt that this fourth
decade of his life had rewarded him with more than rank—
it had enabled him to come to know his family in a way that
was seldom possible to a Navy man who had reached the
pinnacle of the service. When his daughters Jane and Caroline were married in 1841, and he escorted them down the
aisle of New York City's Episcopal Church of St. Marks-in-

the-Bouwerie, it was fine to know that he had been there, at home, to watch over and guide them in their formative years.

Still, broad pennant or no, he was a salt first and always, and when, in 1843, he received command of the new frigate *Saratoga,* he was glad to leave the Navy yard and raise his insignia on the flagship of a squadron that was Africa bound.

His assignment was double—to join the British in hunting down slavers off the Gold Coast, and to destroy certain savages from the Gold Coast interior who were murdering the crews of American merchantmen who stopped to trade with them.

On the Commodore's request more than the usual complement of marines was assigned to his squadron; it was his theory that marines should be more than merely ornamental, and he had a feeling that men who were especially proficient with a musket would come in handy if he ran into trouble with the native chiefs.

The squadron delivered dispatches at Teneriffe, in the Cape Verde Islands. On the way from Teneriffe to the Gold Coast, the Commodore put into effect some of those hygienic measures against coast fever that had so discomfited the bluejackets on his earlier cruises. The men were ordered to sleep in canvas pajamas, and bonfires were constantly roaring between decks. Shore leave was canceled.

The Commodore ignored the grumbling, the muttering and the laughter. "The last laugh will be mine," he predicted to his executive officer. "There won't be a single case of fever in this squadron the entire trip."

The fleet anchored at Monrovia, and the Commodore called on President Roberts of Liberia. Jehudi Ashmun was dead, along with most of the colony's first pioneers, but Liberia itself was a thriving republic. The little colony had a population of almost five thousand, and could point with pride to nine other settlements on its three-hundred-mile coast.

"Liberia is at peace with its native neighbors," President Roberts told the Commodore. "But conditions are less than satisfactory in other colonies along the coast. The Fishmen, the native tribe you have come here to punish, are growing more insolent and belligerent every day. Now they're cornering food and supplies badly needed by the colonists and terrorizing the Bushmen, who have a treaty with the whites. Something will have to be done to curb these marauders if the Gold Coast is to avoid a bloody war."

The flagship *Saratoga* left for Cape Palmas, site of the Maryland Colonization Society settlement. Aboard was a white mare, a present to the Commodore from President Roberts. At Palmas the Commodore meant to acquaint himself more thoroughly with the plight of those colonists troubled by the Fishmen, and meet King Freeman, chief of the friendly Bushman tribe.

King Freeman arrived at his meeting with Commodore Perry dressed in an old Navy uniform coat with tarnished epaulettes, a red cap, and checked trousers. The Commodore kept a straight face, and presented the king with gifts of food and clothing. King Freeman's son, Prince Joe, was taken for a short cruise aboard the *Saratoga*. During his trip the exuberant ten-year-old prince invaded the galley and overturned a huge tureen of soup. He also managed to lather up the walls of the Commodore's cabin with his favorite shaving soap.

The Cape Palmas colony was in sorry shape. The Fishman blockade had deprived it of food and medicine, and coast fever had affected not only the settlers, but their cattle and fowl. At night Fishman warriors approached the settlement and frightened the colonists with their war drums and blood-curdling cries.

The Fishmen were quite capable of taking it into their heads to attack the colony and slaughter every man, woman and child. They had already murdered the entire crew of an American trading schooner, the *Mary Carver*. Shortly after the *Mary Carver* had disappeared, the villages of the savage tribe had sported American flags and seamen's clothing, and in the Fishmen's thatch huts, Bushmen friendly to the white authorities had seen pieces of furniture definitely belonging to the unlucky American ship. There was a rumor that a white sea captain had been roasted to death over a slow fire at Beribi. In recent weeks another American sailor, the captain of the bark *Atlanta*, had been robbed by the Fishmen, beaten, and sent bleeding on his way.

"Before we can move against the Fishmen we've got to take some hostages," the Commodore told his officers. "And that's not such an easy task, since the Fishmen are wary about coming aboard an American warship. My plan is this. We'll close the gunports of the *Porpoise* and run her down the coast disguised as an English trader. Crewmen will dress in Scotch caps and plaid shirts. As soon as the Fishmen come aboard to trade with these innocent Scotsmen, we'll grab them."

The plan worked. Prince Jumbo, one of the fiercest of the Fishmen, came aboard the *Porpoise* at a coastal trading station with five of his men. Realizing their mistake, the Fishmen promptly jumped overboard and tried to swim to shore, but the bluejackets, assisted by some Kroomen canoers, picked them up and clapped the prisoners into irons. The Commodore had his hostages.

He spent the next weeks investigating other aspects of the Fishmen-trader trouble, learning that the blacks weren't entirely to blame. On many occasions whalers had invaded their villages, firing into the huts and abusing the Fishman women for their drunken amusement.

94

As always the Commodore intended to be scrupulously fair to both sides. "I will try to convince these tribes that the government of the United States, while determined to protect the rights of its citizens in pursuit of their lawful business in this part of the world, will be equally mindful to redress any and every aggression by Americans upon the natives."

By late November the Commodore had gathered enough evidence to proceed against them. Anchoring off Sinoe, he demanded a parley with the chiefs of the three tribes involved: the Fishmen, the Bushmen, and the Kroomen, the porters and boatmen of the region.

Seventy-five marines in thirteen boats, along with a detachment of heavily armed bluejackets, accompanied the Commodore to the parley, held in a Methodist church.

The Americans learned that their antagonists were wily and completely unscrupulous men. The Fishmen flatly denied that they had murdered the captain and crew of the *Mary Carver*. "How could we have done such a terrible thing?" asked Prince John of the Fishmen. "We have only love in our hearts for the Americans."

"If you persist in lying," the Commodore replied, "I have only one course, to impose a general fine on all the villages of the coast. This fine will be in effect until you are willing to tell the truth."

The strategy had its desired effect. A chief of the Bushmen stepped forward and said, "There is no reason why we should be penalized for the wrongdoing of the Fishmen. I demand that Prince John confess to the murder of the white men."

Prince John rose in his turn. "I am not permitted to say such important words," the young man said. "Only my father, King George, may make a confession."

"Where is King George, then?" asked the Commodore.

95

"He is not in the village," answered Prince John.

The Commodore sighed. "I don't believe that," he said, and asked the interpreter to find out from the Bushman chief if King George was indeed away from the village.

Receiving the answer he had expected, the Commodore turned to Prince John. "Go get your father," he told him. "You have exactly twenty minutes to bring him here."

King George, a furtive, shambling Negro, arrived and took his seat in the courtroom. "I am not empowered to confess the murders," he said, "since I am only a Half-King. King Nippio is the real King of the village."

Some of the officers laughed, and even the Commodore smiled briefly. "Where is King Nippio?" he asked King George.

The Half-King gestured vaguely. "He has gone into the jungle."

"Listen to me carefully," the Commodore said. "If you do not produce King Nippio in *ten minutes* I will burn the village to the ground."

Seeing that the Commodore was serious, King George agreed to send Prince John to fetch King Nippio. Once clear of the church, however, the long-legged Prince bolted, eluding his guards, and after the general hullabaloo was over, it was discovered that King George had vanished too.

The Commodore confessed himself beaten, for the moment. Holding a few of the Fishmen hostage, he adjourned the meeting until the next day and returned to the *Saratoga* for a badly needed glass of port.

When the palaver resumed the next day none of the native chiefs, Fishman, Bushman nor Krooman, was available; they had all vanished into the jungle. But although his hostages refused to put their 'x' on a paper describing the *Mary Carver* murders, they were willing to admit to the killings verbally in return for their freedom. As the clerk of the *Saratoga*

96

took their statements down, it became clear that the captain of the *Mary Carver* had been far from blameless in the affair. He had tried to seize the Fishmen's canoes without provocation, and thus brought upon himself and his crew the retaliatory wrath of the natives.

That night, aboard his flagship, the Commodore held a council of his officers, and took a vote on whether the killing of the *Mary Carver*'s five-man crew was to be construed as an act of deliberate murder. The officers held that the American traders were at least halfway to blame. However, on the issue of whether the Fishmen must be expelled from the coast region, the officers were in complete agreement with the Commodore, who believed they represented a serious threat to law and order and must be sent back to the interior from whence they had come.

The Commodore sighed. "Much as I'd like to avoid it, I'm afraid we have no choice but to burn the Fishman villages."

Next morning the Commodore marched into the Fishman village at Sinoe with an escort of marines. Standing before King Nippio's thatch hut, he made an announcement: the Fishmen had six hours to move their wives, children and possessions out of the compound. He deeply regretted that he must take this course, but at exactly four o'clock the village would be put to the torch.

As the interpreter finished his translation, a poisoned dart whistled past the Commodore's ear and buried itself in the thatch behind him. His guards leveled their muskets at the crowd, but the Commodore barked out an order, and his men lowered their weapons slowly.

Calmly, looking to neither the right nor the left of him, the Commodore returned to the *Saratoga*, where his officers soon learned he was in a vile mood. At four o'clock the village of Sinoe was burned to the ground, and a few minutes later the squadron raised anchor for Cape Palmas.

97

Native drums had reported the burning of Sinoe village to the blacks of Cape Palmas before the Commodore's fleet arrived, and a messenger was at the landing to tell Commodore Perry that several hundred angry natives were threatening the Cape Palmas stockade.

Quickly the Commodore called a meeting at the house of the colony Governor. The meeting had hardly gotten under way before shouts and screams from outside broke it up.

Commodore Perry demanded an explanation and learned that the natives, discouraged by the arrival of the fleet, had fallen back from the stockade. But that wasn't the problem. A tribesman, charged with loyalty to the whites, was being given the "poison trial" to establish his innocence or guilt.

"If he survives," the Governor explained to the Commodore, "he is innocent, unless he is a warlock—a male witch—in which case his recovery proves he is guilty, since only a warlock could fail to die from drinking poison." The Governor shrugged. "We have to go along with their ridiculous code of justice."

"We do *not*," said the Commodore firmly. "I refuse to allow such barefaced murder!" Calling his guard, he went to the rescue of the unfortunate native.

But there were complications. The trial had been moved across the lake, and though the Commodore and his marines arrived there quickly, the victim had already downed the contents of the poison cup.

"Get him to the ship and give him the strongest purge we have," the Commodore ordered. "He'll be all right." He sat down on a stump and wiped his sweat-streamed face. This comic opera would have been laughable, if so many lives weren't at stake.

If Commodore Perry thought his work was finished for

the day he was mistaken. A burst of gunfire interrupted the dinner the Governor was giving his naval guests, and a courier arrived with news that a band of Fishmen were attacking the stockade.

Mounting his white mare, the Commodore led the marines to their second rescue of the day. The Fishmen melted away at the approach of the superior American force, and the Commodore returned to the executive mansion to finish his plum pudding.

A grand palaver was called at the Cape Palmas mission church for the next day. Represented were Cape Palmas, Liberia, a number of coast missionaries, and the local chieftains of the Bushman and Fishman tribes. Everybody began to talk at once—the whites, who complained of the Fishman boycott; the Bushmen, who charged that the Fishmen had forced them to go along with it; and the Fishmen, who offered a long list of crimes allegedly committed against them by the white traders.

The Commodore pounded for order, and when he had gotten it, allowed each aggrieved party to speak in turn. When each faction had presented its case he delivered his verdict.

"Nobody here is in the right, but the bulk of evidence is against the Fishmen. Peace on the coast is possible only if all the Fishmen leave it. This the Cape Palmas Fishmen must do, selling their lands at a fair price to the Cape Palmas colony. The Bushmen, on their part, must lift the boycott against the colonists and agree to cooperate with them in the future. And the whites must promise to act fairly in all their dealings with the Bushmen. The case of the Beribi Fishmen who murdered the crew of the *Mary Carver* is another case entirely, and will be taken care of at Beribi itself. Court adjourned!"

That night, at another council meeting, the course of action to be taken with the Beribi Fishmen was decided upon, and the next day the squadron left for Rockboukir, the port nearest the Beribi villages. The Commodore called for another grand palaver to be attended by all the chieftains of the area, and the Fishmen sullenly acquiesed.

A pavilion was erected in the middle of Grand Beribi, and the ground rules laid down: both King Ben of the Fishmen and the Commodore would have their private guard with them, and an equal number of marine and native guards would stand outside. This was acceptable to the Commodore; if there was any violence, his pistol and cutlass-armed bluejackets could take care of twice the number of spear-armed Fishmen.

The Commodore opened the proceedings with an ultimatum. "Since the guilt of the Beribi Fishmen in the murder of the crew of the *Mary Carver* is beyond dispute, the chiefs will execute every man who had a hand in it. The Beribi Fishmen, like their fellow tribesmen elsewhere on the coast, must leave their villages and return to the interior. These are my terms and they must be accepted."

A low and hostile murmur started up among the Fishmen, and the marines took a firmer hold on their muskets.

King Ben of the Fishmen, a huge man almost seven feet tall, rose to speak. "O White Chief," he said, "we are innocent of murder. If this is true, then by the justice of the white men you cannot banish us. I swear by my word that the white traders did not meet death by our hands."

This barefaced untruth infuriated the Commodore. He strode up to King Ben and shouted, "How can you disgrace your people with so bald a lie! Tell the truth, man, or I'll drag it from you!"

King Ben could understand no English, but he knew that the white chief was calling his bluff. Enraged, he embraced the Commodore in a bear hug, and began to drag him off to where his iron spear stood, butt down, in the floor. The spear had twelve notches, in token of the number of men the powerful chief had killed with the razor-sharp weapon.

The marines sprang into action, but the burly Commodore had no need of their help; he was a match for the King, and throwing him to the floor, made a break for the doorway. As he hurtled through it he heard the crack of a Marine musket—one of his men had shot King Ben.

The meeting ended in a melee. Natives, pursued by marines, poured from the pavilion, and outside there was equal pandemonium. Hundreds of natives were scattering into the woods, along the beach, and into the sea, jumping into the canoes they had left there. Some turned in their flight to fire at the bluejackets.

The wounded King was finally subdued, bound, and carried down to the beach, where the Commodore had formed his ranks. He called the captain of marines.

"Captain, fire the town. I'm beginning to hate myself because of these poor Negroes, but we've got to take a firm hand."

As the thatch and wattle huts went up in flame the blacks opened fire at the bluejackets from the edge of the woods. Their marksmanship was poor, and the Commodore ignored the nuisance.

"Back to the ship," he ordered. "We'll finish the job from there."

The fleet's cannon routed the Fishmen from the woods, and the little war with the heathens was over for the day. King Ben died that evening, after expressing repentance and offering his twelve wives to the Commodore.

For the next few days the Commodore's men landed at various Fishman villages on the coast, firing them after making sure they had been abandoned. Although the operation had been a complete success, Commodore Perry refused to

101

accept the congratulations of his staff. "I take no credit for routing a bunch of ignorant savages who know no better," he told them. "My only consolation is that there was no loss of life."

The squadron returned to Cape Palmas, where the Commodore sent out another invitation to the Fishman chiefs to foregather. The new Fishman king came aboard the flagship to sign an agreement in which the tribesmen agreed to withdraw, without exception, into the interior. He also promised to punish the men guilty of the *Mary Carver* murders.

One of his officers asked the Commodore how he could be sure the Fishmen wouldn't descend upon the coast again after the American squadron had left it.

"Lieutenant," replied the Commodore, "these are primitive people, and to them scorched villages represent judgment. They won't attack, knowing that the same judgment will follow."

For the next seven months the squadron was on duty off the Gold Coast, searching for slavers. In June, 1844, it returned to Monrovia to find its orders of recall. The five ships of the African squadron arrived at Sandy Hook almost a year to the day they had left it. They arrived "clean," without a single case of fever aboard.

But if he had expected to drop anchor in Newport for a deserved long rest in the bosom of his family, he was mistaken. He came home just in time to take a hand in the realization of one of his longest and fondest dreams: the creation of a national naval academy. When that was established at Annapolis, and he applied again for temporary retirement, his request was rejected on the grounds of "probable developments of crucial nature with Mexico."

The United States had annexed Texas, and Mexico was ready to go to war. President Polk sent a representative to Mexico City in an attempt to settle the differences between the two countries; he was willing to buy, if possible, California and New Mexico. But the war party in Mexico was in power and refused to hear of any agreement that included an American Texas. War was declared by the United States in May, 1846.

For a year before that Commodore Perry had been busy in New York, building new ships for his country's woefully small steam navy. Though over thirty new ships were in progress, the Navy in 1845 could boast only thirty-three craft, including four steamers.

8 ⊏⊏⊏⊏⊏⊏⊏⊏⊏⊏⊏⊏⊏

IT WASN'T TILL SEPTEMBER, 1846, THAT COMMODORE PERRY had the chance to join the fleet off Vera Cruz blockading Mexico's ports. Commodore David Conner was already in command of the Mexican Squadron, and rather than lose this chance for action, Calbraith Perry accepted a demotion, the narrow red pennant of a vice commander, under Conner.

The Vice Commander arrived at Sacrificios Island to find the fleet suffering badly from poor morale. Conner, an overly cautious old man, typical of the old sea dogs who were still fighting the War of 1812, refused to make a move until it was too late to profit by it. Only a month before he had timidly withdrawn from Alvarado harbor at the very moment of certain success. Discipline in the squadron couldn't have been worse. Added to this state of affairs was the fleet's fear of yellow fever and the dangerous northers that appeared with sudden fury and could easily devastate the squadron at its shallow, rocky moorings.

Everyone was complaining, and the Vice Commander had to lecture his sons Matthew and Oliver Hazard on their attitude. Matthew was now a lieutenant in command of the sloop *Raritan,* and Oliver an officer of marines aboard the *Saratoga.* They, along with Lieutenants Farragut and Porter, were angry enough to bring the inefficiency of Commodore Conner to the attention of the Navy Department, and their father had to remind them that while the Commodore was certainly overly timid, he could hardly be blamed for the fact that American warships were meant for combat on the high seas, not for coastal patrol.

Matthew Junior glumly changed the subject. "Father, I mean, sir, do you think we'll capture Vera Cruz?"

Commander Perry shrugged. "That will require the combined operation of both the Navy and the Army. We can only wait for further developments."

These developments weren't long in coming. Late in October Conner sent for his Vice Commander, and suggested the capture of San Juan Bautista, up the Tabasco River, and the taking of the Mexican fleet at anchor there. Could he do it?

The Commander thought for a moment. "How many ships will I have at my disposal?"

"Seven, including the *Mississippi*."

The Commander nodded. "We need the Mexican light-draught vessels to make up for our own lack of them. Commodore, I'll do my best."

As always, the Perry best was much more than adequate. On his way up the Tabasco, the Commander captured the town of Frontera, and two days later arrived at San Juan Bautista. He ordered his vessels to anchor before the city, and immediately dispatched boarding parties to take over the Mexican fleet, composed of a sloop, a brig, five schooners, and several boats. What little resistance the boarding parties encountered they soon disposed of.

The Commander then called in one of his lieutenants. "I'm sending you under a white flag into the city. Tell the commandant, General Bravas, that if he doesn't surrender, I'll level San Juan Bautista to the ground."

A short time later the lieutenant reported back, "Sir, General Bravas says, 'Fire when you're ready.'"

The Commander grunted. "We'll see if the man is as brave as his name."

General Bravas was more talk than fight. At the *Vixen's* first salvo, aimed at the flagstaff of the fort, the Mexican tricolored flag fell, and the Mexicans immediately asked for a parley. But when the marines formed ranks to enter the city the defenders increased their rifle fire, and the Commander ordered his troops back on board the ships. It was nightfall, and they would take the fort tomorrow.

The next morning a party of Mexicans approached under a white flag, and agreed to surrender. However, either the Mexican troops were totally undisciplined or the surrender agreement was a ruse, for they fired upon the American truce party, killing an officer, and snipers shot down at the ships from the fortress loopholes.

The furious Commander Perry gave his orders: "Clear every city street with cannon fire!"

American shells lobbed into San Juan Bautista, doing heavy damage to the fort, the cobblestoned streets and the stucco houses. Finally the fortress was reduced to silence, and Perry, gathering his fleet of captured prizes, left the battered city. As it dwindled behind him he sighed, "Even if we'd had enough men to occupy the place, we wouldn't have had enough arms for them to hold it."

Technically the Americans had failed to capture the city, but at least the enemy had lost part of their fleet, and Vice Commander Perry's squadron was received at Sacrificios Island with salvos and cheers. The news of the battle was rushed to the American papers, where much was made of it, and thereafter the morale of Conner's squadron noticeably improved.

By mid-November the American Army, under General

Winfield Scott, was within striking distance of Tampico, a coastal city that ranked second in importance to Vera Cruz. On November 14 Conner and Perry, with all their fleet, appeared off Tampico Bay. The Mexicans withdrew from the city, the American flag was raised in triumph, and Tampico was occupied without the firing of a shot. But the problem was the same as at San Juan Bautista—there were no forces to occupy the city.

The Vice Commander suggested that he take the *Mississippi*, the fleet's fastest ship, to Brazos Island, and get some troops there from General Patterson. Conner gave his permission. Within ten days six hundred and fifty men had arrived at Tampico to garrison it, but the *Mississippi* wasn't there to take credit for the badly needed reinforcements. It had gone on to New Orleans, and picked up additional cannon and over a hundred men. These arrived at Tampico a week later.

In January Commander Perry brought the *Mississippi* into Norfolk for repairs. He scarcely had time to see Jane at Tarrytown before he was off to Washington to consult with General Winfield Scott, who had left his command in Mexico to come to the capital to discuss the pending campaign against Vera Cruz.

The Commander was strongly in favor of a combined undertaking of the Army and Navy against the key enemy city. Scott agreed with him, as did most well-informed men in the services and the government, but there were others who believed that either the Army or the Navy should try to take the only real stronghold the Mexicans had.

"Tell me," said General Scott, "your real opinion of Commodore Conner. Is he the man for half the job?"

Calbraith Perry had to tell the truth—that he wasn't. Old, sick and timid, Conner should be in retirement, not at the head of the Mexican squadron. If Navy regulations had been enforced he would have left the service four months ago.

What influence Scott had with the President and the Navy Department the Commander never knew nor cared, but by the end of February he received these orders at his Washington hotel:

You will proceed with the U.S.S. *Mississippi* to the Gulf of Mexico, and on your arrival, will report to Commodore Conner, who will be instructed to transfer to you the command of the United States naval forces at that station.

The *Mississippi* dropped anchor outside Vera Cruz just as the Army, assisted by the Navy, landed on Mexican beaches near the city. Conner had done a creditable job in the debarkation, and it was with real regret that Commodore Perry showed him his orders.

Conner looked at them and smiled painfully. "Today the Mexicans began firing on Army troops surrounding the city. I'll be sorry not to be here when we take it."

"But you will," the Commodore said. "I hope to be calling upon you often for advice." He felt pity for Conner; for a soldier or sailor to be relieved of his command was a humiliating thing.

"General Scott is a difficult man," Conner told him. "If I may say so, you may be needing my advice. But I'm grateful for your last words, Commodore. When I see the blue pennant hoisted on your flagship I won't feel quite so badly."

Next morning the Commodore called on General Scott aboard the *Massachusetts*, and offered whatever assistance he could give him.

"I need six heavy Paixhans for use by the army ashore," Scott said.

"Certainly, and I'll be glad to send along the gun crews."

Scott frowned. "My men are good artillerymen, Commodore. They're familiar with the Paixhan. All I'm asking for is the loan of the guns."

What a glory hunter this Scott was, thought the Commodore. Well, he himself was just as anxious to uphold the honor of the Navy, and he owed his gunners trained at Sandy Hook a chance to show their prowess. "I'm afraid that's impossible, General," he said. "In my command the guns are inseparable from their crews."

Scott smiled coldly. "Commodore, are you forgetting the favors I did you in Washington?"

"I didn't ask for them, sir."

The General stood up, trembling with anger. "Perry, you have a ramrod for a spine, and someday it's going to rust away. Good day. If you can't cooperate with me, then the Army will have to get along without you."

"Scott's both stubborn and willful," Conner said when the Commodore told him of their conversation. "You must deal with him gently. General Taylor, on the other hand, can be talked to man to man."

The Commodore nodded. "I've learned that. But I predict he'll come around very shortly, with hat in hand. He needs those Paixhans."

Within two hours the Commodore received a message from General Scott. The General wished to start a general bombardment against Vera Cruz. He would much appreciate it if the Commodore could land his naval guns, with crews. The Paixhans would be set in place by Captain Robert E. Lee, the General's engineer.

The bombardment lasted for three days, and on the last of these Scott's and Taylor's men attempted an assault on the city. Meanwhile the fleet hurled tons of steel on the fortress to soften it up for the hand-to-hand fighting that would be necessary once the walls were breached.

The devastating naval bombardment had shattered the city's walls, and before the infantry could stream inside, the Mexicans raised the white flag. The fortress surrendered at the same time.

It was an easy victory, but there were still other pockets of Mexican resistance to be overcome, chief among them Tuxpan, and its fort at the mouth of the Tuxpan River. Three steamers, three schooners, thirty rowboats and a force of 1600 men made their way up the river in the first of the pageants that were to become so typical of Commodore Perry. While bands played and pennants fluttered, the carefully spaced and precisely rowed boats approached the fort. A cannon boomed, then another, but the fleet pressed forward into the enemy fire. Then the *Spitfire* began its bombardment of the fort, and the Mexican fire ceased abruptly.

"Land and storm!" shouted the Commodore through his speaking trumpet, and the rowboats dashed up on the beach and discharged armed sailors who had undergone weeks of rigorous training. The Americans' guns and their perfect discipline had completely demoralized the Mexicans, who fled both the fort and its protective trenches. The Commodore saw personally to the destruction of Tuxpan fort, added what Mexican ships lay at anchor to his fleet, and then turned downriver again.

When Santa Anna, the Mexican commander-in-chief, heard of Tuxpan's capture he said, "That devil Perry! He conquers not only with shot and shell; he can be victorious with flags and tubas!"

The Commodore still had an old debt to settle with San Juan Bautista. Though his rheumatism was troubling him and Navy physicians warned him against overtiring, he took another fleet of steamers, schooners and rowboats up the Tabasco River.

At Devil's Elbow, Mexican riflemen attacked from the

shore. The *Saratoga* lobbed a 10-inch shell into their midst, and the enemy scattered. The flotilla anchored for the night, continuing up the river at dawn the next morning.

For three days the naval force toiled toward their destination, the prey of insects, Mexican snipers, and unseen snags and obstructions in the river. The Commodore called a meeting of his officers. "I know this snail's pace we're moving at is driving you mad." He swatted at a mosquito. "As a matter of fact, I don't feel all that sane myself."

He held up his hand to still the rather nervous laughter. "I've decided to divide our forces for a simultaneous land and water attack. Captain Rand will be in command of the fleet, and I'll take the land force with six cannon."

There was a silence.

"What's the matter, gentlemen?" the Commodore asked. "Do you have objections?"

A lieutenant clear his throat. "Sir, won't it be difficult to transport heavy cannon overland?"

"Difficult, Lieutenant, but not impossible."

Next morning the land party watched the flotilla disappear upriver and turned to its first task—hauling the six cannon up a steep bank.

A red-faced officer reported to the Commodore that somebody had "forgotten" the cannon limbers, the detachable forepart of a gun carriage, consisting of wheels and axle.

The Commodore's wrath was awful, but the ordnance officer responsible was with the flotilla, and his punishment would have to wait until the land party caught up with it at Bautista.

Stalking to the bank, the Commodore personally directed operation cannon-haul. It could be done only one way, with sailors and marines lifting the stocks off the ground while others pulled and tugged with heavy rope. The combined strength of a hundred men was needed before the cannon

111

were hauled over the lip of the bank and onto the relatively level ground beyond.

A captain of marines requested a rest for his weary men, saying that they were "plumb exhausted."

The Commodore shook his head. "Captain, I'm sorry, but I intend to get to Bautista before the fleet does. We're an hour behind schedule already. There will be no rest till noon."

With the Commodore setting the pace, the land party stumbled its way across the open country. The sun beat down, the insects stung, an occasional rattlesnake had to be disposed of. A sniper wounded one of the sweaty column, and the Commodore took up a musket and brought him down like a bird in a tree.

At noon the Americans came to the village of Acachapan, and took cover as the Mexicans fired on them.

Word came to Commodore Perry that the Mexican defenders were commanded by none other than his old enemy, General Bravas.

"This time I'm going to get the old fox alive," the Commodore told his captain of marines. "You'll attack head-on, and I'll take a flanker to the rear. We'll catch him between us."

But the old fox was up to his old tricks; he withdrew from the village before the Commodore could surround him, and all the marines captured for their trouble were a couple of cowering villagers and a few dusty chickens.

Though the battle at Acachapan was a brief one, it had set back the Commodore's timetable, and he pressed on toward Bautista, showing his troops as little mercy as he showed himself.

When they came in sight of Bautista, the land party was footsore and weary, but they had arrived before the flotilla —by some fifteen minutes. Elated, the Commodore forgot about the punishment of the ordnance officer who had neglected to bring along the cannon limbers.

After giving his troops several hours rest, he ordered the cannon put into position. As the flotilla sent its first shell into San Juan Bautista, the Commodore's cannon roared. For an hour both fleet and land party pounded the city, and then the Commodore sent his men in to attack, telling them to ignore any and all white flags of surrender.

Mexican resistance was slight, and in a short time the marines succeeded in running up the Stars and Stripes over the three forts of the city. The forts were then systematically destroyed, and their guns taken as trophies. Before sundown the victorious expedition was on its way back to Vera Cruz.

The taking of San Juan Bautista was the last naval exploit of the war. Mexico City fell in September, and a peace treaty was signed soon thereafter. In October the Commodore took General Scott back to New Orleans in triumph. Both received a hero's welcome.

Calbraith Perry was frankly glad that the whole messy business was over. The United States had fought wars more just than the Mexican War, and many Americans, with good reason, were ashamed of it. He himself hadn't deserved the laurels of the hero, and neither had anybody else, including Winfield Scott. The most effective antagonists the United States forces had encountered were fever and bad weather, not Mexicans nor bullets.

"We should forget it and go on to better and nobler things," the Commodore told Jane in Tarrytown. "America is too great a country to need such petty victories."

9

IT MIGHT HAVE BEEN AN IGNOBLE VICTORY, BUT THE MEXICAN War added new dimensions to the United States' territories. With Alaska, her western border extended clear to the Pacific Ocean, and with the addition of California and Oregon, American merchants and businessmen saw themselves as sitting in the center of the commercial world, halfway between Europe and Asia.

America was now a power in the Pacific, as well as in the Atlantic, and the State Department, along with powerful and influential merchants, looked forward to an expanded Far Eastern trade. There could be no Far Eastern commerce without bases and coaling stations for the American steamships, and picking likely places for these in the Pacific, statesmen and business leaders were increasingly concerned with the seclusive and mysterious islands of Japan.

There were other reasons why Americans were occupied with thoughts of Japan. For one, the Nipponese were decidedly unfriendly. Storm-buffeted whalers had landed on the Japanese coast only to be forced away at spear and gun point. Ships' crews castaway on the islands had been thrown into prison and forbidden to look upon their surroundings before being hurried out of the country aboard one of the

114

few Dutch ships allowed to dock in Japanese harbors. The handful of Dutch traders permitted to live in Nagasaki were watched day and night by their hostile hosts.

All the major powers of the world had repeatedly tried to provide a basis for peaceful trading with Japan, but all had been rebuffed. In 1825 an English fleet, hoping to negotiate a treaty, had dropped anchor in Yedo Bay, now known as Tokyo. But the British admiral had been told that the Japanese wanted both cultural and commercial isolation, and would, in fact, defend it to the death. Five years later a French fleet had been hurried out of Nagasaki harbor without its representatives having been able to land.

Americans had learned just how fanatical the Japanese isolationists were. In 1831 a Japanese junk, blown by storms, drifted onto the coast of the Columbia River. The shipwrecked crew were treated kindly by their American rescuers, and an American merchantman, the *Morrison,* set out to return them to their homeland. When the *Morrison* entered Yedo Bay in July, 1837, she was fired upon by Japanese land batteries, and after attempting to anchor near another island, was again driven away. It was only then that the good samaritans learned from their passengers that any Japanese who had left his country was forbidden to return!

Eleven years after this an expedition under Commodore Biddle had been sent to Japan to discuss the opening of trade relations with America, but again the haughty Japanese lords refused to trade with the visitors. In 1849 a Captain Glynn, commanding the U.S.S. *Preble* in the China Seas, received word that sixteen shipwrecked American sailors were being held by Japanese authorities. When Captain Glynn entered Yedo Bay he was fired upon and ordered off, but he dropped anchor, insisted upon a parley.

The devious Nipponese wasted so much time in negotiation that Glynn was forced to issue an ultimatum: if the prisoners weren't returned he would take them by force. The Japanese relented, and a few days later the courageous Captain was on his way home with the shipwrecked sailors.

It was evident that the Japanese, though they had a big navy of their own, respected American power, and President Zachary Taylor decided the time was ripe to seek a trade agreement with them. The people were clamoring for action. Ship captains sailing from the Pacific ports were weary of giving the Japanese coast a wide berth, and the whalers were shouting for the right to buy supplies in Japanese harbors, and for protection for their shipwrecked crews.

In 1845 Congress voted to establish diplomatic relations with Japan. Commodore J. H. Aulick was given command of the next Japanese expedition, and under his plan, the American offer to start trade relations was to be made indirectly. Recently a crew of Japanese castaways had been landed at San Francisco, and it was Aulick's idea to pick them up at Macao, where they had been sent from California, and deliver them at Nagasaki. If the Japanese responded in the slightest to Aulick's overtures, he was to suggest that a treaty be signed between the two countries. Aulick carried with him a letter written by Daniel Webster, the Secretary of State, to be presented to the Mikado, in the event that all went smoothly.

On June 8, 1851, Aulick set out for Japan in the new steam frigate *Susquehanna*. He stopped at Rio de Janeiro and at Zanzibar on diplomatic errands. For another three months he was on the China coast, gathering up a squadron of ships to impress the Japanese with the might of the American Navy.

On September 5, Commodore Perry was called to Washington to consult with the Navy Department. Within two minutes of his arrival at Navy Secretary Graham's office he was offered command of the Japanese expedition.

The Commodore went pale. "But sir," he objected, "Commodore Aulick has already been put in command of the expedition."

"We are relieving him," said Graham. "We have information that Aulick took his son aboard his flagship as a free passenger without proper authorization. There are various other charges against him."

"I'm sure he can clear himself of them," said the Commodore. Aulick had long been his friend and he knew him to be a man of the utmost integrity. Command of the Japanese expedition was the post of a lifetime—an assignment that would bring fame to the man who successfully carried it out, and Perry meant to defend his friend, who could accomplish this mission.

"The decision has been made," Graham said drily. "Am I to infer that you are declining the assignment?"

The Commodore shook his head. "Since my enemies will say I betrayed Aulick, I want merely to make it clear that I have already asked to be given command of the Mediterranean squadron. Ever since Conner's recall in the Mexican War, my enemies have accussed me of being a self-seeking opportunist. Now they'll say I used my influence to oust Aulick. I wouldn't want to give them ammunition."

Graham smiled. "Commodore, I'll do everything in my power to spike their guns."

But the Commodore's mind was already on other things. "Mr. Secretary, what ships are at my disposal for the expedition? And it occurs to me—how will I be able to insure a coal supply in the Orient? What—"

The Navy Secretary rose from his chair. "There's plenty of time for planning. You won't be receiving your formal orders for several months. Suppose now we adjourn for lunch. Oscar, our chef, has a special way with lobster."

In late March, 1852, Commodore Perry received his formal

appointment as head of the "Expedition of an American Squadron to the China Seas and Japan." He fully expected to be under way to the China coast within a month, but he was overly optimistic—it would be a whole year before the squadron left New York harbor.

There were a thousand and one things to be done. First he had to choose his ships; the bulk of Aulick's squadron had left the China coast for duty elsewhere, and there were only two frigates, the *Supply* and the *Susquehanna,* awaiting him at Macao. He chose the steamer *Princeton,* and sent it to drydock for the latest improvements in marine engineering. He picked out a new frigate, the *Vermont,* being completed in the shipyards. Three other ships, the *Macedonian,* the *Saratoga,* and the *Vandalia,* were to accompany his flagship, the *Mississippi,* on the Far Eastern voyage.

Before him lay an immense amount of research. In the next months he read every book on Japan he could get his hands on, and pored over maps and charts for the purchase of which the government had appropriated over $30,000. He decided on the gifts he would take to the Mikado; they would be the best products of American manufacture. One of these was a miniature engine and train, a working scale model made by the Philadelphia firm that was building locomotives for American and European railroads. He ordered one of the new American telegraphs, and almost daily the postman groaned under the load of scientific instruments that arrived at Tarrytown. These were some of the wonders of American civilization the Japanese were missing by shutting themselves off from the outside world.

But most of all there were the books, books, books. Often in the early hours of the morning Jane would come into the library to find him asleep at his desk. Shaken awake, the Commodore would refuse to go to bed and launch into an

118

enthusiastic description of what he had learned in his five or six hours of steady reading.

"There were two reasons why Biddle and the others failed. They allowed themselves to be treated as inferiors, and they made no effort to learn about Japanese customs in advance of coming to the islands. The Japanese social order is based upon a rigid caste system—every man is born and dies in his own place—and the Mikado can be approached only by his equal. So, since we Americans as a democratic nation have no caste system, I've go to create one. And, of course, put myself at the head of it. I've already picked out a name for myself: Lord of the Forbidden Interior. How do you like it?"

Jane laughed. "My dear, I just can't think of you as anything but Cal, the distinguished Commodore Perry. And now, my Lord of the Forbidden Interior, I insist that you retire!"

The Commodore went to Washington for talks with Daniel Webster and Navy Secretary Graham. Between them they settled three questions.

First was the scope of the expedition. Its real aim was, of course, a trade agreement with Japan, including the right to exchange diplomatic and consular representatives. This depended upon a treaty of peace between the two nations which would guarantee protection of shipwrecked American sailors, and the right of American ships to put in at Japanese ports for supplies. The Commodore was to go as far as he could in getting as many of these concessions as possible. But at no time was he to use force.

The second objective was the exploration and survey of the Japanese coast and its nearby islands. If America was to trade with Japan, coaling stations were a necessity, as were accurate charts of the Japanese shoreline.

The third objective concerned China. American interests were threatened by disorder on the Chinese coast. When he reached Chinese coastal waters, before going on to Japan,

119

the Commodore was to cooperate with American civil authorities in protecting the rights of American citizens, insofar as this did not conflict with the expedition itself.

Daniel Webster was so impressed by the Commodore's recommendations for handling these matters that he gave him what amounted to carte blanche. He told President Taylor: "The success of this expedition depends solely on whether it is in the hands of the right man. Commodore Perry knows best how it is to be successfully carried into effect. If this be so, then he is the proper person to draft and carry out his instructions."

It was good Daniel Webster had given full authority to the Commodore, for now politics reared its head to obstruct his progress, and if he had been obliged to go to other men for approval of his actions, the expedition might well have withered on the vine. President Taylor died and was succeeded by Vice-President Fillmore. With a new election approaching, Webster resigned as Secretary of State to accept the Whig Presidential nomination, and Secretary of the Navy Graham agreed to be his running mate. The Navy portfolio went into the hands of John P. Kennedy, and that gentleman had little interest in the expedition. Perhaps he was influenced by newspaper reaction to the pending eastern voyage, for almost all of it was unfavorable.

Many newspapers had the impression that Commodore Perry meant to invade Japan by force, and at Tarrytown the Commodore read the various editorials with mounting rage.

"Listen to this!" he barked at Jane, and read from one of the Philadelphia papers: " 'There is no money in the treasury for the conquest of the Empire, and the new administration will hardly be disposed to pursue such a romantic notion.' And here's a sneer from the New York *Herald:* 'The Japanese expedition is to be merely a hydrographic survey of the Japanese coast, so the Navy says. Are we to imagine that the thirty-two-pounders are to be used merely as measuring instruments, and cannon balls to be used for measuring the base lines? If any Japanese is foolish enough to put his head in the way of these meterological instruments, of course nobody will be to blame but himself should he get hurt.'"

Jane picked up her knitting. "I think that's understandable, Cal. Newspapermen can't forget the Mexican War, and they think your expedition is only another piece of land-grabbing. Besides, both the press and the people are interested in other things—the Presidential campaign and the gold rush in California."

The Commodore grimaced. "The opening of Japan, if I succeed in it, will be one of the most significant events of the century, but practically no one sees it that way except me."

"And the application-filers," Jane added, smiling. "Do you know how many letters from office-seekers came in the mail this morning? Over thirty."

He nodded. "I'm glad I insisted that only those who are subject to naval discipline can make the trip. I'll have no civilian interference or political exploitation. I'm not going to repeat Aulick's mistake, innocent as he was, and lay myself open to the kind of gossip that can destroy the expedition. It's too important for that."

Despite additional problems—delay in the outfitting and repair of the squadron that reduced his effective ships to two—the Commodore was ready to set sail in late October. Oliver, appointed his father's personal secretary, had orders to join the expedition in Macao—the Commodore wanted no repetition of the Aulick affair. In early November the *Mississippi* and the *Princeton* left Chesapeake Bay for the Orient. They weren't long under way, only a few hours out, when the *Princeton* broke down with engine trouble, and it was obvious that her engines would have to be completely overhauled. Disgustedly the Commodore put into Norfolk, where

121

he abandoned the *Princeton*, and went on to Washington to arrange for a substitute.

"The *Powhatan*," Secretary Kennedy told him, "will follow you when it can be made ready for sea. I'm sorry about the delay, but at least it gives us a chance to give you an official banquet. Perhaps the President will join us."

"May we forget the banquet, Mr. Secretary?" the Commodore asked a little gruffly. "I'm anxious to get under way. I'll start the cruise alone, with the *Mississippi*."

On November 27, 1852, the Japanese Expedition, composed unimpressively of one ship, steamed past Cape Henry and out to sea.

Commodore Perry stood in the bow, watching the land recede behind him. He laughed. "Well, I could have done worse," he told himself. "I started the eighteen-twelve war in these very waters in a rowboat. Now at least I have a steamer."

The rest of the fleet needed time to assemble off the China coast, and the *Mississippi* steamed a leisurely course eastward, putting in at Funchal, in the Madeiras, and stopping at St. Helena. On January 24 she dropped anchor at Capetown, and on February 3 she started toward Mauritius across seas unknown to the Commodore.

From Madeira, where the *Mississippi* took on coal, the Commodore wrote to the Secretary of the Navy:

As a preliminary step one or more ports of refuge and supply to our whaling and other ships must at once be secured, and should the Japanese government object to the granting of such ports upon the mainland, then it will be desirable that the squadron should establish places of rendezvous at one or two of the islands south of Japan.

The islands called the Lew Chew are said to be dependencies of Japan as conquered by that power centuries

122

ago, but their actual sovereignity is disputed by the government of China. These islands come within the jurisdiction of the Prince of Satsuma, the most powerful of the princes of the empire and the same who caused the unarmed American ship, *Morrison*, on a visit of mercy, to be decoyed into one of his ports and then fired upon. . . .

It strikes me that the occupation of the principal ports of these islands for the accommodation of our ships of war and for the safe resort of merchant vessels of whatever nation, would be a measure justified by both the rules of moral law and the laws of stern necessity.

In my former commands upon the coast of Africa and in the Gulf of Mexico where it fell to my lot to subjugate many towns and communities, I found no difficulty in gaining the goodwill and confidence of the conquered by treating them with both. . . . So I believe that the people of the island will render confidence for confidence and will learn to consider us as their friends.

The letter went on to say:

Thus is it my plan to try out my tactics on the Lew Chews before trying them out on Japan herself. It may be that my anticipations are too sanguine. Perhaps they are, but I feel a strong confidence of success.

It was the State Department, not the Navy, which replied. They wrote:

The President concurs that you should secure one or more ports of refuge. . . . If these cannot be obtained in the Japanese islands without the use of force, it will be necessary for you to seek them elsewhere.

In establishing yourself at one or two convenient points in these islands, with the consent of the natives, you should yourself pursue the most friendly and conciliatory course, and so should all others under your command. Take no supplies except by fair purchase. . . . Prevent all plunder and violence on the part of your men toward these simple and unwarlike people. Let them see from the first that our coming among them is a benefit and not an evil.

The *Mississippi* left Mauritius for Ceylon. Continuing on through the Strait of Molucca, she arrived at Singapore. For the moment it looked as though there was no coal to be had in Singapore, but through a Chinese merchant the Commodore discovered a source of supply. The Commodore had reason to be grateful to the merchant for more than the coal, for through him he met his chief translator and interpreter, Ah Sum.

Before the *Mississippi* raised anchor at Singapore on March 29, the Commodore and the aging Chinese with the beard and twinkling eyes were good friends.

Ah Sum was a scholar who had spent many years studying the Japanese, and from him the Commodore was to learn many things about the yellow people that he had not found in books at home. But the Chinese had more to offer than information and counsel—he was a highly diverting companion who was able to make Commodore Perry laugh. Not only was the Commodore embarked on a mission of the greatest importance and seriousness, but he was a man of much seriousness himself, and since the *Mississippi* had left Chesapeake Bay there had been very little laughter aboard the ship. Ah Sum, with his high spirits and infectious humor, changed all that. He could make even the dullest lecture on the Japanese an entertainment, and often officers of the *Mississippi*, passing the Commodore's cabin on their way fore or aft, would stop to hear the deep rumble of laughter from within. If they stopped to listen, which they doubtless did, what they were likely to hear was something like this:

"There are seven castes of Japanese, Commodore. For you perhaps that is not such a lucky number? Ah so, well, let us proceed. First, at the top, is the Mikado. He has the most illustrious lineage of any royal family in the world, for the first Japanese emperor was on the throne when your friends, the British, were painting themselves blue and going about in animal skins. Sir, I am pleased that you are amused a little. Yes, I will perhaps have another glass of port. . . .

"But to continue . . . Next in order to the Mikado is a group of great nobles. Their titles and perquisites are hereditary, and so the most important posts in the Empire are passed among them from father to son. These are the posts of prime minister, treasurer, first war lord, and so forth. Next to the nobles are the priests, and after them come the military caste. These are the samurai, and they are much like the knights of feudal times. The samurai, the retainers of the great lords, have the right to wear two swords. One is a fighting sword; the other is used for suicide when they have been dishonored. Oh, you will learn much about the Japanese concept of honor, and no doubt it will prove very troublesome to you.

"After the samurai come the professional class—the doctors, lawyers and teachers. They are followed by the artisans, and after the artisans come the merchants. Unlike your country, where the merchant and the businessman are king, the Japanese merchant is without honor. Because he sells for gain he is held in the greatest contempt by the social orders above him. It is only the lowly peasants which he, in turn, can look down upon."

"And there is no class lower than the peasants, Ah Sum?"

"Only one—those whose livelihood brings them in contact with dead flesh. The butchers, the tanners, the garbage collectors. Ah so, if you were even to mention such a person to a Japanese lord, he would be deeply offended."

"You make me feel like a barbarian from the north, which

125

is undoubtedly what the Japanese will consider me. . . . But let us talk of Japanese politics. I understand that the real power in Japan resides not in the Mikado, the Emperor, but in the Shogun, the regent appointed from the ranks of the nobles."

"That is correct, sir. The Mikado is only a symbol. He has no power of appointment or administration. His every movement is watched, and he cannot leave the palace. The Mikado has appeared to the public only on the occasions of his coronation, his wedding, and his death."

"Then it will be the shogunate with which I will be dealing. I won't have the chance to give the Mikado personally the presents I have for him."

"That I would very much doubt, Commodore. And in this regard I should give you a word of warning. You cannot count on the word of a Japanese official. In Japanese diplomacy, promises are just a means of gaining an advantage. It is just another difference between East and West. You will be lied to often, and you will not be able to afford the luxury of telling the truth in return."

"Ah Sum, I'm living a lie already, uncomfortable as it makes me. Back home in America there is no such title as the Lord of the Forbidden Interior."

"Ah, very good! Excellent. That is a fine name you have given yourself. Commodore, I see that you learn very fast!"

The *Mississippi* docked in Hong Kong's exotic harbor on April 6, and was greeted by three American ships—the *Plymouth*, the *Saratoga*, and the *Supply*. But where was the *Susquehanna*, most impressive of the squadron and the man-of-war the Commodore had chosen as his flagship? It developed that a United States commissioner had requisitioned it for a trip to Shanghai, and had also taken with him an American official whose advice the Commodore needed before he left for Japan.

The angry Commodore called for his executive officer. "Send the *Plymouth* on to Shanghai, where it is to order the *Susquehanna* to wait for us. This is going to throw the whole fleet off its course, but I'm glad we're leaving Hong Kong before the week is out."

He spoke too soon; it was only the first of many delays that were to plague him. The Tai-Ping rebellion against foreign settlements was at its height, and influential American merchants, who wanted the protection of the fleet, were understandably reluctant to see it steam off to Japan at this particular moment. Commodore Perry was willing to make only one concession—he would leave the *Plymouth* temporarily on the Chinese coast. This failed to satisfy the American merchants, who wrote Congress about their plight. While the matter was still before the House, the squadron, minus the *Plymouth,* went on to Macao, where Oliver and his father were reunited, then to Canton, which had been chosen as the final rendezvous of the fleet.

Canton disappointed the Commodore. He had expected to find beautiful pagodas, lotus blossoms floating in pools, all the exotic picturesque beauty of the fabled Orient. Instead, as he confided to his journal, there was only "filth, noise, poverty and misery, lying and roguery. The Chinese pickpockets and thieves are the most skillful in the world. Supplies for the fleet vanished as my men loaded them aboard in the most extraordinary manner. One officer had his watch and chain stolen as he bent down to tie his shoe."

Commodore Perry and his chief officers were entertained royally at a fifteen course dinner where Cantonese specialties were served. Despite the hospitality of his Dutch, Portuguese and British hosts, it was all too obvious that the Commodore's rivals wished the expedition bad luck.

"How," asked a Dutch official, "can a nation as young as

127

the United States expect to accomplish a task great nations feel is practically impossible?"

The Commodore, though not known for his wit, was equal to the occasion. "Sir," he answered, "to the young nothing is impossible, as they often are fond of telling their senile elders."

The fleet went on to Shanghai to pick up the *Susquehanna*. There the well-known American author Bayard Taylor came aboard the flagship, begging to join the expedition.

The Commodore told him that all expedition members were forbidden to write for later publication in magazines and newspapers, and that even the diaries kept by his men were the property of the Navy Department. "Nor," he added, "am I permitted to take on civilians."

"But you can take on additional members of the crew," Taylor persisted. He smiled slyly. "I hear that your son Oliver was added to the expedition this way in Macao, so as to prevent charges of favoritism before the squadron left the States."

The Commodore sighed. "All right, Mr. Taylor, you've convinced me. Sign the ship's articles. But I warn you, you may not like the bos'n's discipline."

On May 17, six days before leaving Shanghai for the Japanese off-shore islands, the Commodore wrote his wife:

My dear Jane,

I write a few lines to say that we are all well—Oliver is on board and has begun his duties. The cocky Bayard Taylor is also one of my unofficial guests.

The Governor has sent me as a present a piece of straw colored silk which I shall send home by the first vessel of the Squadron returning to the U.S., along with some tea and a few trifles for the children.

There is little new, except that one of my ships has gone aground and will have to be floated safely off; I hesitate to employ any of the Chinese for this, fearing that my pocket will be picked during the operation, but I suppose we must take some chances in this life. . . .

Ah Sum, who saw your picture, says you are the most beautiful American female he has ever seen. I trust you are still carrying on our famous egg-rollings Sundays on the front lawn.

Your affectionate husband,
C.

On the afternoon of the twenty-third, with a large crowd watching on the river bank, the five-ship squadron, with the *Susquehanna* in the lead, left for the waters of Japan.

Three days later it anchored at Napha, the port of the largest island of the Lew Chews, today known as Okinawa. "How green and beautiful!" Bayard Taylor remarked. "Like the richest English scenery."

At that moment the author saw a boat coming toward the flagship from the island. His eyes widened with surprise: the boat was flying the English flag. What in the world was an Englishman doing on this island?

He was soon to find out. Aboard the boat was an English missionary named Bettelheim, a converted, Austrian-born Jew who had been sent to Napha some years before by a group of religious and philanthropic Britishers.

The Reverend Bettelheim, a rather strange-looking man with a large, bulbous head and a nervous way of talking, was full of complaints. "I never should have come to Napha," he told the Commodore. "Sir, one doesn't stand a chance with these Japanese. I've managed to convert only two of the heathen, and do you know why? One of them was a spy, and the other stole my entire wardrobe." He sighed like a martyr. "If you only knew the slights I've suffered. These people have only contempt for foreigners."

The Commodore saw that Bettelheim was eying his bottle

of sherry, and he poured the missionary a glass which he downed gratefully. Glancing out the porthole toward the shore, the Commodore saw that his squadron was being watched carefully by a group of natives. "Pretty suspicious bunch, aren't they?" he commented to the clergyman.

"Sir, you can't imagine! If you only knew what my wife and I have gone through on this God-forsaken island!"

"I see a boat's put out from shore with two rather important-looking personages. Reverend, would you interpret for my executive officer? My Chinese interpreter is indisposed with a cold, and it's my policy to deal in person only with the highest officials."

The missionary accepted the opportunity to be of service eagerly. From his cabin porthole the Commodore watched the two officials come aboard. They were dressed in long robes of blue grass cloth, and around their waists were orange sashes. On their heads were yellow box-shaped hats, and they wore sandals. Though youngish men, they had long black beards. They bowed low to the executive officer, and presented to him a yard long roll of Japanese red paper. Then the visitors returned to their boat via the ship's ladder.

"They are disappointed you would not meet with them after they had presented their salutation of welcome," Bettelheim told the Commodore. "They said they would come again tomorrow."

"They'll get the same reception," the Commodore said. "I will meet only with the Regent of the Lew Chews."

The missionary nodded. "Your method is a wise one. To ignore his minor dignitaries is the only way to get the attention of the island Regent himself."

The Japanese officials returned next morning with gifts of pigs, fowl and vegetables. The gifts were rejected, and again Commodore Perry refused to receive the dignitaries, one of whom was the Mayor of Napha.

As the officials' boat headed for shore, the Commodore saw several Japanese junks leaving the harbor. Northbound, their destination could only be Japan. The Mikado, or the powerful lords around him, would soon be hearing of the American fleet anchored off the Lew Chews. His plan was proceeding on schedule.

Later that day, without having bothered to get the islanders' permission, several boatloads of the Commodore's men landed on Napha to explore, buy supplies, and rent a house on the island. Reporting to Commodore Perry in his cabin, the officer in charge of the landing party told him that the natives had definitely refused to rent the Americans a house.

"Not that I expected them to," the Commodore said. "Lieutenant, were the natives at least polite?"

"Aye, sir, too polite. They put on a show of good-natured ignorance that, I believe, masked a thorough comprehension of our reasons for coming to the islands."

"Of course. They know it's my intention to establish a base here in case the Mikado refuses to let me enter Yedo harbor."

But the next day the aged Regent of the Lew Chews did pay a call on the American commander. As the old man stepped aboard the *Susquehanna* with a crowd of his retainers, the ship fired a seven-gun salute. In terror the Japanese dropped to the deck on their knees. Many of the *Susquehanna* crew, lined up in dress uniform, found it impossible to repress their laughter.

After waiting for a good half hour, the Regent, with two of his staff and the Reverend Bettelheim, were shown into the Commodore's quarters.

The Regent and the Commodore greeted one another ceremoniously and cautiously, neither too certain of the other's importance and rank. Cakes and wine were served,

131

and then one of the Regent's retainers took out two pipes, which were passed to the Regent and the Commodore.

After puffing on his pipe for a moment, the Commodore turned pale and glassy-eyed. He turned to Bettelheim and whispered, "Reverend, are they trying to drug me?"

Bettelheim smiled and shook his head. "It is opium you are smoking. I would advise you to put the pipe down. You have smoked enough to satisfy protocol."

The Regent and the Commodore began a general conversation, during which the American was invited to a reception ashore the following Monday.

"Tell the Regent," the Commodore said to Bettelheim, "that I accept with pleasure, and will arrive at Shudi palace with my party at the time specified."

As Bettelheim translated his remarks, the Commodore was surprised to see that they had thrown the Regent and his officials into a veritable dither. Good Heavens—they were chattering like a couple of magpies! He watched as they drew back to consult with one another under their breaths.

"What's the matter?" he whispered to the missionary.

"Sir, do not take offense, but the situation seems to be that only persons of the highest rank can be received at the palace. Never before has a barbarian set foot there. The Regent wishes to receive you at his home."

Sick of this barbarian talk, the Commodore reddened with anger. The snobbishness and exclusiveness of these Japanese was beyond belief! "Well, Reverend," he told Bettelheim, "you may say I'm determined to make my visit to the palace at Shudi, and I expect a reception in accord with the dignity of the great nation I represent. You may also add that our conversation for today is over."

The Regent received the ultimatum in silence, not saying whether it was accepted or rejected, and bowing low, he filed from the cabin with his party.

Bettelheim wiped his brow. "Sir, that was touch and go for a moment. Are you sure you did the right thing?"

Ah Sum emerged from behind the door where he had been standing for the last half hour, giving the Commodore signals. Grinning, the Commodore introduced him to the astonished Reverend.

"Ah Sum," the Commodore said, "has told me of the Dutch merchants in Japan, and how they kept their right to trade there only at the price of the worst kind of servility and knee bending. The Japanese are accustomed to treating all foreigners with the same contempt. Well, they're going to learn that Americans don't accept that kind of treatment."

Ah Sum, who still had a bad cold, sneezed.

Now it was Bettelheim's turn to grin. "Do you know," he said to the Chinese, "I heard somebody sneeze behind the door there, and for a moment I thought it was a Japanese spy! Especially since the Regent and his men didn't seem to hear it!"

10 ᗧᑎᑎᑎᑎᑎᑎᑎᑎ

THE RIGMAROLE WITH THE REGENT CONTINUED. NEXT DAY A
messenger arrived at the *Susquehanna* with a message from
the old man. Ah Sum translated it to the Commodore: the
palace, for several reasons, was in no condition to receive so
august a personage as Commodore Perry. Would he therefore allow himself to be received in Napha, rather than at
the royal palace at Shudi?

The Commodore sighed in exasperation. "Ah Sum, send
him a reply as follows: 'Commodore Perry does not accept.'"

The same afternoon the Mayor of Napha asked the Commodore to a great feast at his home on the day preceding that
on which the Commodore expected to appear at the royal
palace. He was about to accept when Bettelheim was shown
into his quarters.

"Commodore," said the missionary, "I have some information for you. The Regent plans to appear at this feast to
which I understand you have been invited, and afterwards
he plans to claim that this meeting with you at the Mayor's
home amounts to an official return of the Regent's visit to the
flagship."

The Commodore threw down his pen and lifted his hands
above his head despairingly. "These wily Japanese stop at

134

nothing! Thank you, Reverend. Ah Sum," he said to the Chinese, "write the Mayor another one line letter saying that the Commodore regretfully declines."

The Regent's bag of tricks wasn't empty. On the day of the banquet twenty Japanese arrived at the flagship bearing the dishes that the Commodore and his officers would have eaten, had they attended the banquet.

"He's made us guests *in absentia*," the Commodore said, and ordered that the food be served to his men. "Please write the following message," he told Ah Sum: "The Commodore thanks the Mayor for the food, which his men have found delicious. He himself, however, did not touch it."

"What do you think the Regent's next move is likely to be?" the Commodore asked Ah Sum later. "This comic opera is making me dizzy."

Ah Sum shrugged. "He will not give up so easily; he has his Japanese overlords to contend with. Naturally he does not wish to lose his head on the block. My guess would be that he will try to arrange the reception at the palace of the young prince for whom he is Regent. Doubtless he will have some convincing excuse, but I would not believe it for a minute."

Ah Sum was right. A day later another messenger arrived from the Regent suggesting that the reception be held at the palace of the young prince Akhito. It was explained that the dowager queen, who lived at the royal palace, was ill and could not be disturbed. A British naval officer had visited her recently, behaving in such a loud and boisterous manner that the queen had been badly upset. She still had not recovered.

"I doubt if the dowager queen exists," Ah Sum said. "With your permission I will go ashore and attempt to find out with the help of Reverend Bettelheim."

"By all means," the Commodore said.

Ah Sum returned in an hour. "There is no dowager queen," he said, "at least at the moment. She died five years ago."

With tongue in cheek the Commodore penned a reply to the Regent. "I regret the ill health of Her Majesty, but must respectfully submit that if she has received an officer of low rank of the British Navy, she cannot, without dishonor to the great nation of the United States, refuse to receive an Admiral of that country's Navy. Perhaps, should the dowager queen find it inconvenient to move to the prince's palace, it is possible that the music of our marine band will lift her spirits. Perhaps, too, she would not find it amiss if my personal physician visited her and prescribed for her ailments."

The Regent was a fighter, but he knew he was licked. He sent a last message, naming the royal palace at Shudi as the place for the official reception. Smiling broadly, the Commodore called his staff in for a conference. "We're going to have a real parade," he told them. "The advance guard will will be made up of officers in full dress uniform, marines bearing arms, and our more impressive looking sailors. The band will follow, leading another company of marines. This company will be my guard of honor. I shall be sitting in a sedan chair, the most imposing sedan chair any ship's carpenter ever built on two days notice. Following me will be seven coolies, bearing gifts for the queen dowager and the prince."

"But sir," said one of the officers, "I understand there *is* no queen dowager."

The Commodore pretended to scowl. "Lieutenant Contee, do you doubt my ability to create one?"

The young officer was flustered. "Yes, sir. I mean no, sir. Sir, I'm rather confused."

The conference broke up in laughter.

The Commodore's parade was a great success. The townspeople of Napha had never seen such pomp and ceremony,

136

and they crowded wide-eyed around the procession as it made its way to the royal palace. The feasting lasted till early morning, and even the Regent forgot his worries long enough to thoroughly enjoy himself. Since she was not well, the queen dowager failed to appear.

The Commodore had forced the Japanese to accept him as an equal, and for the rest of their stay at Napha, life was much easier for the Americans. Spies still hounded them, and the townspeople would answer no questions, but they were able now to buy supplies, and no obstacles were put in their way when they brought their ships in closer to shore to overhaul them for the trip to Japan. The maneuvers and target practice the Americans engaged in made the Regent rather nervous, but he accepted the Commodore's explanation that such military drill was routine for the squadron, and did not mean that the Americans planned to attack Yedo when they arrived there.

Before leaving for Japan the Commodore took the *Susquehanna* on a six-day sail to the Bonin Islands. He had hoped to establish a coaling station on the islands and claim them for the United States as a base for American shipping, but he found that the British had been there before him. The Union Jack flew over a motley settlement of thirty-odd English, Americans, Portuguese and South Sea Islanders. The Bonins were an object lesson to the Commodore—how was the United States to enlarge its power in the Pacific if its own State Department hadn't even known that the British had taken over the islands?

He returned to Napha to learn that the old Regent had lost his job. "The overlords did not like it," Ah Sum explained, "that the American fleet, instead of departing with drooping sails, is still in Lew Chew waters."

The Commodore nodded. "It's perfectly clear that the Japanese have no intention of receiving me at Yedo harbor."

Standing in the bow of the *Susquehanna*, the Commodore watched his squadron leave Napha with mixed feelings. It was July 1853 and he had hoped to be in Japan at least a month ago. Things were going far from well. A fleet of fourteen men-of-war had been promised to him and he had only four vessels; the *Supply* was staying on at Napha and the *Caprice* had been sent on to Shanghai for repairs. Ever since he had entered Hong Kong harbor he had been bedeviled by forces beyond his control.

But the worst of it was that some of his younger officers were calling him a vain popinjay and a pompous egotist. Why couldn't they realize this was no tea party and he would get nowhere with his antagonists unless he acted as he did? Why was he fated always to be unpopular with his men because he insisted on shipboard discipline and measures that were essential for their health, or because he made use of the trappings of his authority? What were such trappings for?

He sighed heavily. Well, at least his men respected him, and he would have to settle for that.

He wouldn't have blamed another man for being overwhelmed by the various problems that faced him. He was trying to establish peaceful relations with a nation that would undoubtedly resist him by force; a nation that over three hundred years ago had expelled with bloodshed the last white man who had tried to enter it uninvited. Once he gained entrance, if he did, he must negotiate on terms of equality with a ruling class that was deeply contemptuous of all foreigners. He must negotiate a treaty which would recognize the equality of foreign merchants, and the Japanese held their own merchant class in even lower esteem than they did most non-Japanese people.

These were hard and unblinkable facts, and for a moment his confidence wavered. He thought how much easier it

138

would have been at Port Mahon as Commander of the Mediterranean Fleet. A life of balls, dinners, diplomatic receptions. The most comfortable, glamorous command in the Navy. The constant presence and support of his wife. . . .

"Commodore, a thousand yen for your thoughts."

He turned; it was Oliver Hazard, handsome, young and smiling. Oliver had a distinct resemblance to his dead uncle, and for a moment—how it made his heart pound!—he thought it was his brother standing here beside him.

"I was thinking, Ol—" he began, and then stopped, biting down on his tongue. Now was no time for doubts and second thoughts, especially in the presence of his son. He must be an example to young Ol, always. Would his brother Oliver ever have given way to despair, no matter how black the outlook, how fierce the storm? He smiled at himself. At fifty-nine he was still comparing himself to his famous brother, and to his own discredit.

"Yes, Father?" Oliver said.

The Commodore cleared his throat. "I was thinking that as the Commodore's secretary, you shouldn't have so much free time on your hands. Have you recopied the program for Independence Day I wrote out yesterday afternoon?"

"Aye, sir," Lieutenant Perry grinned.

"Have you arranged for extra grog rations in the forecastle?"

"I have, sir."

The Commodore scratched his head. "When was the last time you wrote your mother?"

"Last month, sir. And may I remind you that I am fast approaching the legal age of adulthood."

The Commodore ignored his son's last remark. "Below to your cabin, Lieutenant, and break out the pen and ink. We can't have your mother worrying."

"What about my wife, sir?" Oliver said mischievously,

getting in the last word. He had disappeared down the companionway before his father's boot could make contact with his hindquarters.

The squadron celebrated Independence Day with an eighteen-gun salute, special dinners for the officers and men, and extra grog for the bluejackets. Three days later the American fleet had penetrated well into Japanese waters. The Commodore saw to it that there was constant gun drill and clearing for action, and the crews were ready for any and all contingencies.

On the night of July 7 the squadron stood off the entrance to Cape Idsu, the promontory of Yedo Harbor. Beyond it was a range of low mountains shrouded in mist. At dawn the next morning the Commodore and Oliver stood in the bow of the *Susquehanna* as the flagship, leading her three sister vessels, moved slowly ahead. The fog lifted and the Commodore gasped as the majestic white cone of Mount Fujiyama stood revealed against the sky.

"Ol," the Commodore said, "isn't that magnificent?"

Oliver grinned. "All I can think of at the moment is how Mount Fujiyama will look on the postage stamp commemorating your expedition."

Several fishing junks, leaving the harbor for the open sea, were completely unprepared for this huge monster of belching smoke and churning paddlewheels bearing down upon them. They had never before seen a steamship, and, terror-stricken, the small boats scattered in every direction—some putting back towards the harbor and others scurrying out to sea. One demoralized junk captain steered directly into the path of the *Plymouth*, and his men had to drop their sail and take to the oars in order to avoid being crushed against the bow of the American dreadnaught.

After the *Susquehanna's* initial sprint the Commodore ordered his engineer to slacken speed; he wanted to anchor at Yedo Harbor close to noon, when a maximum audience could be expected. The mist lifted as the squadron reached the Cape of Sugami, a few miles from the inner harbor. Commodore Perry was on deck with Ah Sum as the summer sun blazed down upon the harbor, bringing bay and shore-line into brilliant relief.

The Commodore looked upon the scene with admiration and wonderment. "It's as different from the maps of Yedo Harbor I've studied, as a painting is from a daguerreotype," he told his friend. "I've never seen water so blue, nor hills so picturesquely beautiful. The thatch of the peasants' huts is white as snow. And Fujiyama—how magnificent!"

"You have not mentioned those long white buildings," Ah Sum said. "Undoubtedly they are fortifications?"

The Commodore laughed. "If they're not fortifications, they're something close enough to it. Ah Sum, you realistic old coolie, you don't have a shred of romance in your soul! Forget the fortifications for a moment. Let yourself drink in all this loveliness and beauty."

Ah Sum shivered. "There is an old Chinese proverb," he said. "'One can enjoy beauty only when there is no knife at one's throat.'"

A deck officer appeared at the Commodore's elbow. "Japanese guard boats setting out from shore, sir. Have you any orders?"

"Yes. No Japanese are to be allowed on board, whatever their errand. If they're troublesome, keep them off with pikes and cutlasses. Break out the ammunition and post sentries, but there must be no firing upon the Japanese under any circumstances. I want no repetition of what happened on the *Morrison*."

As the officer hurried away there was a loud report from somewhere in the hills, and a sky rocket arched high in the air, to vanish in a cloud of smoke. "Probably a signal that

141

we've entered the harbor," the Commodore said. "They're just a little late."

The Japanese began to beat their war gongs as the squadron drew nearer to Uruga, the village on the left shore of the bay. The racket was terrific, and the Commodore could see that the eerie sounds were doing the strained nerves of the American sailors no good. He passed the word to stand easy.

Now the ships were passing the strange white fortifications on the headlands, and up close they were even more puzzling than before. Instead of forts they seemed to be long swathes of muslin draped on rackframes, with black stripes to give them the appearance of gun ports.

The Commodore lowered his glass. "Sham forts to frighten off the would-be invader, or screens to mask the movement of troops. Or who knows—maybe they're supposed to break musket fire." He smiled. "Our small-arms fire would pass through twenty thicknesses of muslin. That's no way to stop us."

A mile and a half from shore the fleet dropped anchor. The crash of the huge anchors was loud enough, but the *Plymouth* chose that moment to loose a powerful blast from its whistle. As if in response, a signal gun fired, and a new swarm of guard boats put out from shore.

The Commodore squinted through his glass again. "Evidently these boats are prepared to wait us out—they've got water, provisions and sleeping pallets aboard." He handed the telescope to Ah Sum. "Can you make out what those small flags signify?"

"Some boats belong to the army, others to the government," Ah Sum said. "Now the largest one is heading directly for your flagship."

"I'd better go below," the Commodore said. "It wouldn't do for the great Lord of the Forbidden Interior to be in plain sight of an ordinary army officer or government official."

142

From his cabin the Commodore kept in touch with what was going on outside in the harbor. Though warned not to approach the ships of the American fleet, some of the Japanese guard boats had come alongside, and at the *Saratoga* an officer held up a scroll of paper which the Americans refused to receive. Japanese trying to climb up the anchor chains of the *Plymouth* were held off by pikes and cutlasses. One Japanese succeeded in throwing a message aboard the *Mississippi*. It was written in French, and it ordered the squadron to leave the harbor immediately.

One of the Japanese bedeviling the *Susquehanna* was especially persistent, claiming that he had important business with the American chieftain, and finally the Commodore gave Ah Sum permission to speak with him.

The first question of the Japanese was whether the newcomers were Americans. Ah Sum nodded in answer.

"I wish to speak to the leader of the squadron," the Japanese said.

"You cannot," Ah Sum replied, and added haughtily, "The Lord of the Forbidden Interior can be approached only by the highest officials."

This was something of an insult, but the Japanese officer decided to let it pass. "The Vice Governor is present," he said. "Is this dignitary of sufficient rank to speak to the Commodore?"

Ah Sum consulted with Commodore Perry. "Ask him," said the Commodore, "why the Governor himself isn't available."

"The Governor," the officer said in reply to Ah Sum's question, "is not allowed to go aboard foreign ships in Yedo Harbor."

Ah Sum knew he was being trifled with, and was about to break off the talk when the Japanese suggested that the

143

Commodore designate a subordinate of rank equal to that of the Vice Governor to treat with him.

"This is a chess match, not diplomacy," the Commodore sighed, and gave permission to Captain Buchanan, one of his aides, to talk with the Vice Governor.

The Captain, with Ah Sum interpreting, was friendly but firm. Asked again if the Vice Governor might see the Commodore, he refused with a definite shake of his head. "The Lord of the Forbidden Interior," he said, "has come to Japan to deliver a letter from the President of the United States to the Mikado. He desires that a representative of the Emperor, of suitable rank, be summoned to receive a copy of it, and also that a day be set on which Commodore Perry may deliver the original of the letter in person to the Emperor."

The Vice Governor replied: "You must go to Nagasaki. It is the only place where my government can receive foreign communications."

"That the Lord of the Forbidden Interior will not do," answered the Captain. "He has come to Yedo Bay because it is more convenient to the Emperor's palace." Buchanan knew that if the Commodore conducted negotiations at Nagasaki, he would be forced to do so in the presence of the Dutch traders, a jealous lot, and on the same inferior terms which the Dutch already suffered in Japan.

While he had been speaking, the Captain had failed to notice that the Japanese guard boats had been moving in closer to the fleet, but Ah Sum brought them to his attention.

"I demand," the Captain said, "that these boats be withdrawn immediately. If you do not do so, we will be forced to fire upon them. We are here not as your enemies but as the representatives of a great and friendly nation."

The Vice Governor spoke to an aide, who went to the side and shouted down to the officer in charge of the guard boats. The order to withdraw was passed among the fleet of boats, but Captain Buchanan noticed that there were still several of them gathered around the *Saratoga* and the *Plymouth*.

"We refuse to be kept under guard," he told the Vice Governor. "Unless your remaining boats are withdrawn, we will have to disperse them forcibly. And they must stay withdrawn."

It was another decisive moment. Before this no foreigner in Japanese waters had dared to make such a demand. The Vice Governor hesitated, but then barked out an order. In another few minutes the remaining guard boats had withdrawn.

The Vice Governor turned to the Captain. "I can promise nothing about your Lord's letter," he said, "but I agree to pass on his wishes to my superiors."

The Vice Governor's boat disappeared in the twilight. Captain Buchanan gave his report, and the Commodore commended him for the way in which he had handled himself with the Japanese official. Then he called in his executive officer.

"Double the watches, stack muskets on the quarter-deck, and load all boats with pistols and cutlasses. We must stand ready to repel attack. Are the guard boats still withdrawn?"

"Aye, sir. All of them stand at a respectful distance."

"Good. Fire the nine o'clock gun as usual. And at dawn tomorrow send out patrol boats to survey the coast."

The nine o'clock gun caused a panic-stricken beating of gongs on shore, and a rush to the village shrines, where the villagers prayed for deliverance from the invaders. But there was no attack. At two in the morning the Commodore turned in, satisfied that his first day in Japan had ended peacefully.

He was less optimistic about the second. More guard boats had arrived during the night, and lined the shore. In the hills the Japanese had thrown up breastworks and armed them with cannon. Still, a boatload of artists had anchored near the *Susquehanna* and were sketching the ship, which led the Commodore to believe that, for the moment at least, the Japanese were more interested in gathering information on the fleet than in trying to destroy it.

Before noon two barges, one of them quite large, arrived at the *Susquehanna*. Aboard the latter was the Governor of Uruga. The Commodore ordered that Captain Buchanan receive the Governor and his party with proper ceremony, and retired to his cabin.

The Governor immediately took the initiative in the ensuing conference. The letter from the President, he said, could not be delivered directly to the Emperor but must be transmitted through the Dutch at Nagasaki. Furthermore, American boats must cease patrolling the coasts; such was strictly forbidden by Japanese law.

The Captain was brief in his reply. "The letter must be delivered at Yedo, your Excellency. I will show you the gold and rosewood box in which it lies. As for our patrol boats— you must understand that the laws of the United States require that we survey harbors in which our ships have anchored."

Before the bewildered Governor could digest this last point, Captain Buchanan showed him the magnificent box in which the President's letter reposed, and the Governor was properly impressed—a people capable of presenting so fine a gift could not altogether be barbarians. Cordially he offered to supply the fleet with whatever water and refreshments it needed.

"Thank you, but we need nothing," replied Buchanan. He went on: "When will we receive your answer as to whether the Lord of the Forbidden Interior may deliver a copy of the letter in Yedo?"

In four days, the Governor said. The question must be discussed in council at Yedo.

"But Yedo is only three hours away," protested Buchanan, responding to Ah Sum's nudge. "Four days is too long a time to wait."

Compromising, the Governor said he would deliver the answer in three days time, and then he and party left the *Susquehanna*.

"We got more than we gave," the Commodore said to Ah Sum. "The Governor called on us, not we on him, and he knows we have no intention of sharing the low status of the Dutch."

The next day, Sunday, the gaping observers on the shore were treated to a show of Christian religious observance. On every deck of the squadron bluejackets stood in orderly rows to hear the chaplain read the Bible from his red-velvet covered altar. Three hundred voices roared out "Nearer My God to Thee," and the listening natives were much impressed. That afternoon a barge approached the *Susquehanna*, and a high Japanese official asked permission to come aboard. "Tell him," the Commodore ordered Captain Buchanan, "that it's the Christian sabbath, and that no visitors can be received."

On Monday bloodshed between the Americans and the Japanese was only narrowly averted. The Commodore had sent out boats to survey the coast near Yedo, and dispatched the *Mississippi* to protect them. Immediately more than a thousand Japanese troops set out in guard boats after the surveying parties and surrounded them. The situation was an explosive one. The guns of the big American steamer leveled on the guard boats, and aboard the survey boats the command was given to fix bayonets. Swords flashed on the decks of the Japanese vessels.

But good sense prevailed on both sides, and the guard

147

boats finally allowed the survey parties to return to their work under the guns of the *Mississippi.* Again the Japanese had been bested. Though vastly outnumbered, the Americans had stood their ground, and penetrated close to Yedo Harbor.

The next morning, in a rich barge with black-striped sails, rowed by thirty oarsmen, the Governor arrived at the *Susquehanna.*

"I regret," he told Ah Sum and Captain Buchanan, "that the copy of the Commodore's letter has been mislaid. May I have the original of it so that I might take it to Yedo myself?"

The Chinese looked at the Captain and the Captain winked imperceptibly; neither believed that the copy of the Commodore's letter had been mislaid. This was just more oriental trickery.

"I cannot give you the original," Captain Buchanan told the Governor. "*That,* as you well know, must be delivered by the Commodore himself to the Emperor."

The conversation was back at the exact point where it had started, and Captain Buchanan reluctantly began it anew. Three hours later he had reached a compromise. Instead of delivering the letter to the Emperor, whom the Commodore had come to admit was well-nigh unapproachable, it was agreed that Commodore Perry would deliver the original at Yedo Bay to the highest court official in Japan. The meeting would be confined to the delivery of the letter, and no other subject would be discussed.

"I suppose," the Commodore said to Ah Sum later, "I should be satisfied, at least for the moment."

Ah Sum nodded. "Up till now it would have been unthinkable for the highest Japanese official to meet with a barbarian, however important the latter might be in his own country."

Next afternoon the Governor came aboard the *Susque-hanna* with a sandalwood box which held a document wrapped in velvet. The document had the seal of the Emperor himself, and was the credential of the Imperial representative, Prince Toda, First Counselor of the Empire. He and the Commodore would meet tomorrow at a special building being erected in Gorihama village, about two miles from Uruga. Was this satisfactory to the Commodore?

Captain Buchanan excused himself to confer with the Lord of the Forbidden Interior. The Commodore, it turned out, was more than pleased. Prince Toda was one of the few high-ranking Japanese known to the outside world; in the United States his status was equivalent to that of the Secretary of State.

"Fine," said the Commodore. "Keep the conference going for a bit and meanwhile send out a survey boat to see if the water around Gorihama is deep enough to accommodate our entire fleet. I'll attend no meeting which can't be covered by our guns. If the Governor wants to know the reason for the survey, tell him that under no circumstances could the Lord of the Forbidden Interior allow himself to be rowed from here to the meeting place in an ordinary ship's boat. And be sure to serve the Governor and his aides plenty of alcoholic refreshment."

The survey boat returned with the information that the water near Gorihama was deep enough to accommodate the entire squadron. After several glasses of brandy mixed with sugar, the Governor and his party were in no condition to notice the survey boat's departure and return. Nor did the Governor object to the American fleet's close approach to Gorihama village. The squadron worked late into the night on preparations for the morrow. Small arms were polished till they shone; the commanders of drill units were briefed and rebriefed; the Commodore conferred long in his cabin

149

with Ah Sum and his chief officers. At one in the morning he called in his weather officer, Lieutenant Blake.

"Well, Lieutenant, what's your unofficial forecast?"

"Fair and clear, sir. A bright blue sky and a mild wind."

"Lieutenant Blake," the Commodore said, grinning, "if you're wrong, I'll hang you from the nearest yardarm."

11

THE MEN OF THE AMERICAN FLEET WOKE NEXT MORNING TO
find that during the night the Japanese had been far from
idle. The entire shore front of Uruga was lined with ornamental screens stenciled alternately with brilliant scarlet
flowers and the Emperor's coat of arms. Crowds of natives
dressed in their holiday best carried varicolored flags and
streamers, and pushing through them were hundreds of
soldiers in scarlet dress uniforms, carrying swords and spears.
The bright sunlight glinted off their shields and helmets.

As the squadron, led by the *Susquehanna,* steamed toward
the meeting place, the crowds followed it on the shore,
shouting and beating gongs. On the decks of the American
ships the officers and men stood in precise ranks, seemingly
composed and observing perfect discipline; none of the
Japanese could have suspected that only an hour ago there
had been a near mutiny when lots were drawn to choose the
300-man guard of honor that would accompany the Commodore and his staff ashore.

Eight Japanese guard boats, flying banners of scarlet and
white, escorted the American ships around the headland of
Uruga toward Gorihama. Here the Japanese display was
even more brilliant. Beautiful paneled screens in every color

of the rainbow ranged the shoreline, and among the larger houses the Americans could see the newly erected Council House—a large building of light wood and paper with three, high tapering roofs. The Council House was surrounded by tall standards from which flew long flags of scarlet and white.

A huge crowd had gathered to witness the ceremonies on both sides of the path that led from shore to Council House. Several divisions of Japanese soldiers, each dressed in distinctive regimental colors, lined the shore. Before them, in the water, bobbed over a hundred guard and patrol boats.

Gorgeously attired, the Governor and his officials arrived at the *Susquehanna* to escort the Commodore and his party ashore. Their lace, silk and brocade far outshone the gold and blue of the American officers, but the latter were consoled by the appearance of the Vice Governor, who was so extravagantly arrayed that he was immediately tagged "the Jack of Trumps."

As the brass band of the flagship struck up, fifteen boats filled with bluejackets set off from the anchored American warships. Halfway to the shore the rowers shipped their oars, and a loud thirteen-gun salute roared from the squadron. A shout went up on shore. Descending to his barge from the gangway was the Lord of the Forbidden Interior, a large, imposing figure of a man in blue uniform with impressive gold epaulettes.

Commodore Perry entered the barge and the five-boat escort rowed at a dignified pace for the mainland.

The Commodore's face was expressionless, but inside his thoughts seethed. This was perhaps the most important moment of his life. How would it go off for him? Would any of his officers make a crucial mistake—would he? Did the Japanese plan to betray him, mean to fall upon his troops and massacre them to a man? He shook his head to banish

152

such preoccupations; above all he must appear confident before his men.

The barge was about halfway from shore when the first boat, containing Captain Buchanan, reached the landing. Major Zellin of the Marines was next to land. As the crews of the other boats disembarked they formed a double line, reaching from shore to Council House. It was through this line that the Commodore would pass. The honor guard were all taller than the average Japanese, and a ripple of admiration swept the native audience, most of whom were no taller than the shortest midshipman in the squadron.

No flicker of emotion crossed the impassive faces of the well-trained Japanese soldiery. They were perfectly at ease. True, their armament of swords, spears and matchlocks was much inferior to that of the Americans, but only three hundred of the barbarians had come ashore, and there were more than five thousand of their hosts, including infantry and cavalry.

"Present arms!" shouted an American officer as the Commodore's barge arrived at the landing. In one single motion the oarsmen held their sweeps at the perpendicular. From the stern of the barge the tall, erect figure of Commodore Perry made its way to the landing plank.

For a moment he stood there, looking straight before him. Then, as if fully aware of the gravity of this moment, he stepped slowly ashore.

With the Governor leading the way, the procession moved from beach to pavilion. First came the marines, followed by the sailors. After them walked the Commodore, with a bodyguard of the ten biggest men in the fleet, and two slight midshipmen carrying the gold and rosewood box. Two heavily armed, magnificently uniformed Negroes, the first seen in Japan, strode beside the Commodore with their bayonets at the ready.

153

At the entrance to the pavilion the guard of honor presented arms. The Governor entered the pavilion first, followed by the Commodore, with Ah Sum, his bodyguard, his chief officers, and the two box-carrying midshipmen. Entering the large, heavily draped foyer, one of the nervous youngsters stumbled, and the Commodore gave him a quick smile of encouragement.

The foyer led to an inner chamber decorated in violet silk. From a crimson divan at the end of the chamber, rose two solemn, elderly men lavishly dressed in gold and silver brocade. They bowed, then resumed their seats without a word.

"His insignia identifies the one at the left as Prince Toda," Ah Sum whispered to the Commodore, as an attendant advanced and placed a gilt and lacquer table before the two Japanese. "The other official is Prince Ido of Iwami."

Prince Ido told Ah Sum that he was ready to receive the documents, and the Chinese passed this information along to the Commodore.

Commodore Perry advanced to within five paces of his hosts. Then he nodded to the midshipmen, who came forward and placed the rosewood box in his hands.

The Commodore showed the two Princes the elaborate seals attached to the box with gold silk cords. Then the Commodore broke the seals, took the two letters from the box written on vellum and bound in blue silk velvet and laid them on the lacquer table.

Prince Ido reached forward and picked up the two letters. He opened the first from President Fillmore, then motioned to his interpreter. The Japanese bowed low, and began to translate the letter:

Great and Good Friend I send you this public letter by Commodore Matthew C. Perry, an officer of the highest rank in the Navy of the United States, and commander of

154

the squadron now visiting your Imperial Majesty's dominion. . . .

I have directed Commodore Perry to assure your Imperial Majesty that I entertain the kindest feelings toward your Majesty's person and government, and that I have no other object in sending him to Japan but to propose that the United States and Japan should live in friendship and have commercial intercourse with one another.

The Constitution and laws of the United States forbid all interference with the religious or political concerns of other nations. I have particularly charged Commodore Perry to abstain from every act which could possibly disturb the tranquility of your Imperial Majesty's dominion. . . .

The Commodore knew the President's message by heart, and as the interpreter translated it into unfamiliar Japanese, he watched the faces of the Princes for their reaction. For all the emotion the Japanese showed, these great noblemen sitting before him might have been graven images. The translator continued:

The United States of America reaches from ocean to ocean, and our Territory of Oregon and State of California lie directly opposite to the dominions of your Majesty. Our steamboats can go from California to Japan in eighteen days.

I am desirous that our two countries should trade with each other, for our mutual benefit. If your Imperial Majesty is not satisfied that it would be safe to abrogate the ancient laws of Japan which forbid foreign trade, they might be suspended for five or ten years, so as to try the experiment. . . .

I have directed Commodore Perry to mention another thing to your Imperial Majesty. Many of our ships pass every year from California to China; and great numbers of our people pursue the whale near the shores of Japan. It sometimes happens, in stormy weather, that one of our ships is wrecked on Japanese shores. In all such cases we ask, and expect, that our unfortunate people should be treated with kindness, and that their property should be protected, till we can send a vessel and bring them away. We are very much in earnest in this. . . .

These are the only objects for which I have sent Commodore Perry, with a powerful squadron, to pay a visit to your Imperial Majesty's renowned city of Yedo: friendship, commerce, a supply of coal and provisions, and protection for our shipwrecked people.

We have directed Commodore Perry to beg your Imperial Majesty's acceptance of a few presents. They are of no great value in themselves; but some of them may serve as specimens of the articles manufactured in the United States, and they are intended as tokens of our sincere and respectful friendship.

May the Almighty have your Imperial Majesty in His great and holy keeping!

In witness whereof, I have caused the great seal of the United States to be hereunto affixed, and have subscribed the same with my name, at the city of Washington, in America, the seat of my government, on the thirteenth day of the month of November, in the year one thousand eight hundred and fifty-two.

> Your good friend,
> Millard Fillmore
> Edward Everett, Secretary of State

Prince Toda, his face still expressionless, handed the second letter to the interpreter, who translated it into Japanese, reading:

I understand that the propositions submitted through me to the Government of Japan are of such importance, and involve so many momentous questions, that much time will

156

be required to deliberate and decide upon their several bearings.

I therefore declare myself willing to await a reply to the propositions of the President until my return to Yedo Bay this following spring, when I confidently hope that all matters will be amicably arranged, and to the satisfaction of our two nations.

> With profound respect,
> M. C. Perry,
> Commander-in-Chief of the United States
> Naval Forces in the East India, China,
> and Japan Seas.

The Governor then knelt before Prince Ido, who gave him a scroll to be presented to Commodore Perry. It was in Japanese, and the Commodore asked Ah Sum to translate it into English.

The letter was as follows:

The letter of the President of the United States of North America is hereby received and delivered to the Emperor. Many times it has been communicated that business relating to foreign countries cannot be transacted here in Uruga, but in Nagasaki. Now it has been observed that the Admiral, in his position of Ambassador to the President, would be insulted by it. The justice of this has been acknowledged, and consequently the above mentioned letter is hereby received, in opposition to the Japanese law.

Because this place is not designed to treat of anything from foreigners, so neither can conference nor entertainment take place. The letter being received, you will therefore leave here at once.

As Ah Sum read the Commodore kept his face impassive. The Japanese message could have been considerably more friendly, but he could congratulate himself on having antici-

157

pated his reluctant hosts' invitation to depart their shores. Altogether the meeting had gone off as well as could be expected. At least he had been received in Japan by representatives of the Emperor.

"Tell the Princes," he directed Ah Sum, "that I shall return in the spring."

"With all four of your ships?" was Prince Ido's question.

"No, with my entire squadron," replied the Commodore, and waited for the Prince's objection.

But there was no official objection. The Japanese got to their feet and bowed low, signifying that the interview was over. Outside the pavilion the procession formed again, and the Commodore was escorted to his barge in the bay.

The *Susquehanna's* executive officer was waiting for the Commodore in his cabin.

"Sir, we're ready to weigh anchor for Napha. Should I signal the fleet to that effect?"

The Commodore sat down. "New orders, Captain. We're leaving in the direction of Yedo. We'll anchor nine miles up the bay from Uruga. My intention is to show our ships to the Japanese capital while the President's letter is being considered."

Commodore Perry ignored the look of consternation that came over the Captain's face. He knew what he was thinking: this piece of braggadocio would imperil all the gains they had made so far with the Japanese. "Tell Captain Buchanan," the Commodore said, "that I'd like to have a word with him."

When the fleet anchored near Uruga there was a great beating of gongs from the shore and at least a dozen signal guns sent reverberations into the hills. An hour later the Governor came aboard the flagship, bristling with indignation.

Captain Buchanan had been thoroughly briefed by the

Commodore. "Commodore Perry," he told the Governor, "does not feel that the Americans have broken faith by anchoring near Uruga instead of leaving Japanese shores. He did not, in any case, commit himself one way or the other. However, you may rest assured that he will leave after surveys are made for the fleet which will return in the spring. In the meantime he will make no effort to land. He has asked me to invite you and your staff to a party this evening aboard the *Susquehanna*."

Though the Governor accepted the invitation stiffly, and with misgivings, the party was a great success. The guests even tried dancing to American music by the Marine band, and it was two in the morning before they departed. In accord with Japanese custom, they carried away with them what food had remained unconsumed.

Eight days later the survey boats had finished sounding for safe channels and outlining the contours of the coast. At dawn on Sunday, July 17, the fleet set sail for Napha. The crew had made many friends at Uruga, and the shore was lined with waving natives. Many of them cried. "The Governor wept also," Ah Sum told the Commodore. "He was very sorry to see the Americans go."

"You mean the Americans and their very fine music and whiskey," grinned the Commodore.

The trip to the Lew Chews was a rough one, with fog, storms and heavy head winds. On July 25 the squadron hove to in the roadstead of Napha. The Commodore went to bed for a badly needed rest and slept around the clock.

In his absence things had gone far from well at Napha. The Lew Chewans had evidently received orders to thwart the Americans, and now they evaded the question of a treaty. On August 21 the Commodore sailed to Macao. There he ran into irritations of a different sort.

159

The source was double—from both his own countrymen and European competitors in the Far East. American merchants were more concerned with the protection of their interests against the Chinese rebels than in the opening of Japan. Meeting with the Commodore on the *Susquehanna,* the United States Commissioner to China, the choleric Adam Tompkins, insisted that he help him with a show of strength that would aid the Commissioner in winning diplomatic recognition from the Chinese Imperial Government.

The Commodore gave Tompkins a steely look. "Sir, my first job is to overhaul my ships for their return to Japan next spring. Nothing will stop me in that task."

Tompkins kept his temper with difficulty. "Commodore, I have many friends in Congress."

"You proved that to me before. I am sure you are a very popular gentleman. However, it is principle that interests me, not popularity." The Commodore rose from his chair. "Good day, sir. I trust you can find your way to the gangplank."

The Commodore survived the new political storms at home that Tompkins brewed for him; his partial success with the Japanese had earned him a certain amount of immunity. By fall, he had received abundant evidence that the nations of Europe, encouraged by that success, intended to emulate it.

The rumors were that the French frigate *Constantine,* which had suddenly left Macao for an unspecified destination, was on its way to Japan. A Russian fleet anchored in Macao and its Admiral came aboard the *Susquehanna* to tell the Commodore that he was under orders from his government to accompany the American fleet back to Japan. The Commodore could do nothing about the *Constantine,* but he could, and did, do something about the Russians and the

British, who were complaining that the Americans had been snooping in the Bonins.

"Sir," he told the Russian, "you may have orders from your government, but I have received none from mine. Though I respect the Tsar, I must remind you that I owe my allegiance to President Fillmore."

The British had to be satisfied with a curt denial of their charges by Captain Buchanan.

Commodore Perry was nonetheless disturbed by these developments. "Our foreign friends are trying to get the benefits of our expedition for themselves," he told Oliver Hazard. "My only course is to return to Yedo Bay before spring. The fleet's assembling satisfactorily at Hong Kong; now we have nine ships instead of four."

But there were inevitable delays, and it was mid-January before the fleet set sail for Napha.

At Napha seeming disaster struck. A Dutch sloop arrived with a dispatch from the Governor-General of Batavia. The Japanese Government had asked the Dutch to tell Commodore Perry that the Shogun—the head of Nippon's ruling party—was no longer living. In view of that fact, and in consideration of Japan's mourning customs, official negotiations would have to be "indefinitely" postponed. It would therefore be useless for the Lord of the Forbidden Interior to return to Japan.

The Commodore called in Ah Sum and showed him the dispatch.

"Do you believe it?" he asked the Chinese. "We both know the Dutch have had a monopoly on Japanese trade for two centuries. They'd like nothing better than to see the American expedition fail."

Ah Sum frowned. "It is hard to tell. The Shogun may be dead; on the other hand, he may not be. Do we have time to find out before leaving for Japan?"

"No. I'm weighing anchor as soon as possible."

"Commodore, is that entirely wise? If the Shogun has indeed died, and if you return before the specified time, the Japanese nobles will say that his death was caused by the Americans, who angered the gods by landing."

"I'll have to take that chance," said the Commodore.

The Shogun was indeed dead, and had been succeeded by his son Iyesada, thirteenth of the Tokugawa line. The Commodore had no way of knowing this for certain, just as he had no way of knowing that his death had assured the signing of a treaty with the Americans. Their cause was won.

Although he had been ignorant of the fact at the time of his first visit, there had existed in Nippon a persecuted but influential minority of Japanese political leaders who were completely in favor of the opening of Japan. These were the progressives, and for a century their scholar-leaders had been in conflict with the hereditary ruling families, allied with the priests and samurais, who dominated the Emperor and the throne. The purpose of the progressives was to regain for the Imperial office the power it had lost to the ruling class, which had maintained its favored position by means of ruthless force and repression. Part of this repression had been the prevention of any Japanese intercourse with the outside world. The nobles knew that to open the eyes of their people to the rest of the world meant, inevitably, the end of their power and privilege. Thus it was equally the purpose of the progressives to bring Japan into the family of modern nations.

For some time the progressives, though threatened with torture and death, had been pounding away at certain evident truths. The first was directed at the military, and concerned the undoubted fact that a primitively armed Japan, out of touch with advances in modern military science and weapons, was an easy prey to any foreign aggressor who

might storm her shores. The second was the equally undoubted fact that the landowning nobles had a great deal to
be gained in learning up-to-date foreign methods of farming
and manufacturing.

By 1852 the progressive thinking element among the Japanese was giving increased consideration to the arguments
of the liberal progressives. There was crisis when the news
came that Commodore Perry had sailed from China and that
he intended to sign a trade treaty with the Mikado. Within
a short time of the Commodore's arrival at the Lew Chews,
the Japanese court knew of his presence. The nobles had
girded themselves to repel the invader, and a number of
leading progressives were thrown into jail.

When the Commodore left Japan, saying he would return
in the spring, the nobles had called a convention of Japan's
four hundred ruling families. As could be expected, the decision was to prepare for war, and the nobles were confident
they had utterly destroyed the progressive opposition. But
then the Shogun died, and the new Shogun Iyesada, a man
of liberal sympathies, immediately reversed the tide. A treaty
of peace favorable to Japan must be signed with the Americans, he told the Emperor, and with his approval made this
possible by forming a cabinet made up almost exclusively of
members of the progressive party.

Though Iyesada was a liberal, he was first of all a Japanese. He wanted the most favorable arrangement possible
with the Americans, and his officials were instructed to get it.
They were to be as wily in negotiation with the Commodore,
as the Commodore had been with them.

On the afternoon of February 13 the Commodore's eleven-
ship squadron dropped anchor near Yedo. A Japanese dignitary came aboard the flagship *Powhatan* and was greeted
by Captain Buchanan and Ah Sum. The Lord of the Forbidden Interior was, as usual, incommunicado in his cabin.

The Japanese was brief. Why had the Commodore not anchored at Uruga, where officials of the Emperor were waiting to treat with him? There could, he said, be no parley this close to Yedo.

Captain Buchanan sighed. The Japanese were up to their old tricks again.

"The Commodore," he said, "wishes to use this particular anchorage, chosen by him on his last trip to Japan. He will not return to Uruga. That is definite."

"I will return tomorrow with the answer of my superior," the official replied, and left the flagship.

"I think we have reason to be cautiously optimistic," the Commodore told his staff at a meeting that night. "The Japanese could have refused to treat with us altogether."

Next day the Japanese returned with a compromise—the meeting, they said, should take place at Kama-Kura, a small village twenty miles closer to Yedo than was Uruga.

Commodore Perry told Captain Buchanan to refuse. "They're trying to maneuver us into making the first concession. Well, we won't. We haven't come back to Japan as supplicants."

"But sir," Buchanan protested, "this petty debate might drag on for weeks. The Japanese already feel that we distrust them. It's the officers' opinion that we should accept the Japanese terms, before they begin to feel we've insulted them deliberately."

The Commodore smiled at the Captain, but there was an edge to his voice as he said, "Captain, I command this expedition. No doubt there has been, and will be, much criticism of me among my officers and men. I would be the last to forbid such criticism. But the ultimate responsibility is mine, and the decisions will be mine also."

Seven days later the Japanese announced that the High Commissioner had arrived at Uruga and was ready to parley

164

with the Americans. The Commodore refused the invitation. Desperately the Japanese reminded him that the Emperor insisted the meeting place be either Uruga or Kama-Kura, but the Commodore stood firm.

"Your men are calling you a stubborn mule," Ah Sum told him. "Some are thinking of complaining to the State Department."

The Commodore grinned. "I wouldn't advise that. A mule has quite a kick."

The Governor of Uruga arrived the next day and was greeted with shouts and backslapping. He was very glad to see his American friends. He begged Captain Buchanan to persuade the Commodore to meet with the High Commissioner at Uruga.

"It's hopeless," Captain Buchanan told him. "If he heard the world was ending tomorrow, the Commodore would still insist on having his own way."

"The Japanese played their high card with the Governor," the Commodore told Ah Sum. "Now I'm going to play mine. I'll take the squadron so close to Yedo that I can hear the ring of the city bells."

"Is that not dangerous?" Ah Sum asked. "Yedo will be thrown into a panic. Perhaps the forts will open fire."

"If they do I don't intend to fire back," smiled the Commodore. "Just think how regretful the Japanese will be that they've misread my intentions. Why, they'll hand me the Empire on a silver platter!"

The Japanese forts were silent when the Commodore steamed into Yedo Harbor, but his move had the desired effect. The following morning the Governor of Uruga came on board and casually announced that with the consent of the Lord of the Forbidden Interior, the village of Kanagawa, a mile from Yedo, would be the site of the conference in two days time.

165

Captain Buchanan tried to hide his smile of triumph and excused himself for a word with the Commodore. He was back very quickly with his consent. That night there was a celebration aboard the *Powhatan,* and some very shamefaced officers admitted among themselves that they had badly underestimated their chief.

On the morning of March 8 seamen of the American fleet, looking shoreward, saw a large pavilion surrounded by colorful screens. More screens, leading from pavilion to shoreline, formed a passageway down which the Americans would pass. The water between shoreline and American squadron was almost black with Japanese junks and guard boats.

Exactly at nine o'clock a huge three-masted barge appeared from down the bay and steered its way through the American fleet to the landing place. The American seamen gaped at its canopied decks and brilliantly flagged pavilion. Slowly, like a floating palace, it bumped into place at the landing. It took more than twenty minutes for its occupants —five Japanese High Commissioners and their retainers—to disembark.

A signal was given from the *Powhatan,* and from all eleven ships of the squadron, boats put off toward shore. They carried five hundred officers, seamen and marines, all in full dress uniform. As soon as these men had been drawn up in ranks around the landing, a seventeen-gun salute thundered from the fleet, and the Commodore set off in his barge from the flagship.

The Commodore's barge passed through a lane formed by fifty ships' boats, in which the crews sat at attention with oars erect. As he stepped ashore on Japanese soil for the second time, the small howitzer in the bow of each boat barked out a noisy salute, and the band on shore played the *Star Spangled Banner.* A group of nobles in scarlet and white came forward to meet the Commodore, each bearing the

166

feudal banner of his family. One had three elaborate women's hats in a circle, another a pair of spectacles resting on an open book. The curious emblems made several of the sailors snicker, but when the Commodore's eyes sought the culprits, there was perfect silence, broken only by the exclamations of the huge native crowd. Slowly he and his party made their way to the pavilion.

The council room was larger than that at Gorihama, and more ornately decorated with banners, flags and heavily embroidered fabrics. Since it was winter, charcoal burned in copper braziers suspended from the ceiling, and the windows were sealed with oiled paper. Glass, evidently, was unknown in the islands of Japan.

An attendant bowed toward the long settees placed at the left of the door, and Ah Sum chuckled softly. "Commodore," he whispered, "you have won. The Japanese have come here not to parley on your expulsion, but to sign a treaty."

"How do you know?" whispered the Commodore.

"We are sitting on the left—the place of honor in Japan."

The Commodore had little opportunity to savor his feelings of triumph—the five High Commissioners entered the room. Ah Sum was given a message of welcome from the Commissioners, inquiring about the health of the Admiral and his officers, and the Commodore gave a suitable reply. Tea and cakes were served, followed by pipes of tobacco.

One of the High Commissioners handed the Mikado's reply to President Fillmore's letter to Ah Sum, who passed it on to the Commodore. In return Commodore Perry gave to the High Commissioners a copy of the as yet unsigned American-Chinese treaty, to be considered as the basis of a treaty with Japan.

After the Japanese had said that this matter would be given their early attention, the Commodore made a request

167

that stunned his hosts. A crewman had died aboard the *Mississippi*. Might the Americans have the Commissioners' permission to bury him on shore?

The Commissioners withdrew to discuss privately this unprecedented proposal. They mulled it over while the American party was served lunch. Thirty minutes later the Commissioners emerged to grant the request; the American seaman might be buried on the grounds of a Yokohama temple. After a final cup of sake the first conference was adjourned, with the understanding that the second would be held the next day.

Back in his cabin aboard the *Powhatan* the Commodore watched impatiently as Ah Sum opened the Emperor's letter. "Come on, old friend," he told him, "those seals can't be as tricky as all that."

"Sir," the Chinese said, "Japanese seals, like the Japanese people, always very tricky."

The Commodore eyed Ah Sum intently as he read the letter. "Well, what does it say?"

"Very little," Ah Sum said. "The letter is courteous, and offers the Emperor's friendship. But it makes no statement about anything, aside from the information that the Shogun has recently died and his successor intends to observe Japanese law like his predecessor. The Emperor is also willing to supply your fleet with enough food and supplies to aid its immediate departure."

The Commodore banged his fist down on the table. "Immediate departure! I like that! I thought you said they were willing to sign a peace treaty!"

"Oh, but they are," Ah Sum assured him. "These are just more tricks from a bag which has no bottom. You must have patience. Has not a second conference been arranged for tomorrow?"

168

"Yes," the Commodore grumbled. "But it might be for the sole purpose of determining whether I've read the Emperor's letter."

"I think not, sir," Ah Sum said.

"I hope not," the Commodore said grimly, and rang for a bottle of port. His nerves needed some calming.

12

AT THE NEXT DAY'S MEETING THE JAPANESE SAID NOTHING about the immediate departure of the American fleet, and they discussed a possible treaty in a more or less amicable way. Conferences continued for the next three weeks, from eleven o'clock in the morning till one in the afternoon. Negotiations were carried out by letter at these meetings, and the rest of the time was spent in translating the many Japanese documents and in writing replies in English, which Ah Sum then translated into Japanese.

"Japanese policy is certainly clear," the Commodore said to his adviser. "The Nipponese are willing to sign a treaty, but they mean to yield no more than they absolutely must."

The Chinese nodded. "And to this end they are determined to use any and all weapons at their command, including postponement, procrastination and vagueness."

"They offer no proposals themselves, but wait for mine, and then whittle them down so much that they become quite invisible to the naked American eye."

Ah Sum smiled. "There is a proverb, Commodore: 'He who would whittle with an old whittler must have a very sharp knife—and a grindstone under his shirt.'"

In the days to come the Commodore was forced to weigh

every detail of negotiation with the exactness of an honest butcher. It was as necessary to wring from the Japanese the right for Americans to walk unguarded in the treaty village as it was to establish their right to tread American soil. He had to be sure of that concession, so that no Japanese officials could come aboard the flagship to tell him that while the Americans were permitted to land, they were forbidden to move about beyond the shoreline.

The Commodore refused any and all compromises until the Japanese granted him the above right. All of these negotiations seemed endless and did not endear him to his men who were weary of Japan and eager to go home. There was renewed grumbling about the Commodore's stubbornness and shortsightedness, and the reports of criticism that Oliver Hazard brought him sometimes made the Commodore shake his head in bewilderment.

"In the Navy of the future a commander will probably have to issue bulletins on policy to his men. Ol, have you any suggestions on how I should handle this problem?"

Oliver shrugged sympathetically. "None, father. You'll just have to let posterity be your judge."

In the next days the Japanese High Commissioners readily agreed to a general treaty, but they stood firm against granting the Americans the right to establish trading ports. The Americans, they said, could make Nagasaki their port of entry.

In vain the Commodore repeated, "I have told you that we do not intend to remain on the same level as the Dutch, whom you have treated like criminals. We want at least three ports into which we can enter freely—Hakodate in the south, Simoda at Yedo Bay, and Napha."

The Japanese finally gave in on Hakodate and Simoda, though they refused Napha. Japanese sovereignty over the

Lew Chews, they said, was only partial. The Commodore would have to make his own treaty with the Lew Chews.

Though at first the Japanese were stubborn in their refusal to allow American consuls in Japan, under the Commodore's battering they finally agreed to permit two of them to take up residence in the treaty ports. However, at least a year would have to pass after the signing of the treaty before the consuls would be allowed to land.

The High Commissioners were more yielding on the issue of commercial rights and the treatment of seamen stranded in their country. The former were granted, in principle, and the Commodore came away with the guarantee that American seamen washed onto Japanese shores would enjoy a reasonable amount of freedom. Much more important was the inclusion of the "most favored nation" clause, which provided that any other trade concessions made in the future to any other nation by the Japanese, would automatically apply to the Americans. The Commodore knew that after he left the country, representatives of other nations would swarm in to reap the benefits of his pioneer work.

The negotiations were completed on March 15. For days before, the natives had been pre-empting places on the shore for that feature of the treaty talks which they found most important—the landing of the American presents. Hundreds swarmed around the American tars and craftsmen setting up the mechanical gifts for display, and many of the over-eager Japanese fell off the crowded docks into the water.

There was a lot for the wide-eyed natives to see. A miniature railroad, complete with engine, coaches, tracks and siding. A telegraph with a mile of wire. A daguerreotype, a plow, a harrow. American vegetables, with packets of seeds to be had for the asking. Cannon, rifles, swords and small arms. Clocks, perfumes, books, a telescope and navigation charts. An American stove and kitchen sink. And a hundred other articles of American manufacture, made in American cities from New York to Puget Sound.

During the installation of the telegraph, guards had to keep back the curious crowds. Amazed Japanese officials communicated with one another at opposite ends of the wire, and one was so overcome with shock that he fainted dead away. Another refused to believe his senses, and ordered that runners be dispatched to see if they could catch the message as it fled over the wire to its destination a mile distant.

Of all the exhibits the railroad proved most popular. Though many of the less educated considered it nothing less than a demon which would surely kill them if they trifled with it, several nobles took seats on the roofs of the coaches, and whirled around at fifteen miles an hour, eyes shut in delight and with robes flying.

Japanese artists wandered among the booths, making India ink sketches on mulberry-bark paper, which were later used in the writing of popular poems, cartoons and songs. One of them drew a good likeness of Ah Sum, which was later sold in Yedo with the title, "The Wise Man of China Who Spoke for the Americans."

The Emperor had gifts for the visitors from the United States, and the Commodore and his ranking officers were invited to the treaty pavilion to receive them. The Americans found the Japanese workmanship highly impressive. There were bolts of magnificent silks and brocades, delicate porcelain dishes and figurines, lacquer boxes, tables and trays. Not least was a collection of fifty Japanese dolls dressed in various national costumes. One package, beautifully wrapped in mulberry-bark paper, contained a dried fish; another, three tiny Japanese dogs. One officer opened a small package which held a note giving him the right to collect three tons of rice.

"This is not a joke," Ah Sum told the Commodore, "but evidence of the Emperor's high esteem. The Emperor's gifts to his favorites have always included a fish, a dog, and a grain of rice."

The officer received permission from the Commodore to take his rice aboard the *Saratoga*, but admitted he didn't know how the job could be done. Three tons of rice, in 125-pound sacks, was a lot to carry.

The Japanese, however, were ready with a solution. An official signaled, and into the room trouped twenty-five Japanese suma wrestlers, mountainous men of tremendous strength who casually lifted two sacks at a time. One balanced a sack on his head; another somersaulted down the dock with a rice sack held in his arms. In no time at all, the rice was loaded.

On March 27 the Commodore celebrated the conclusion of the treaty with a grand banquet aboard the *Powhatan*. The sixty-five Japanese officials invited, including the five High Commissioners, were not disappointed. A twenty-gun salute greeted the panjandrums, who were then treated to a small-arms exercise and gun drill. They inspected the engine room, and then the banquet of bullocks, sheep, game and poultry was served while the band boomed out military airs.

The merrymaking lasted for an entire afternoon. Many toasts were drunk, and then the Commodore himself announced a minstrel show given by Negro seamen of the fleet. Though the Japanese sense of humor was very different from the American, the minstrel show was a huge success. Nipponese officials were especially delighted when the Commodore presented them with commemorative banjos.

At five o'clock the revelry ended, with the Japanese tucking their unfinished portions into their sleeves. In farewell, High Commissioner Matsusaki threw his arms around the

Commodore's neck, crying, "Nippon and America, all have same heart!"

When the guests had departed the Commodore ruefully examined his crushed epaulettes. "Well," he told Oliver Hazard, "I guess I should be glad the old suma wrestler didn't break my back."

Within the next three days the Commodore and the Japanese High Commissioners signed a treaty which admitted Japan to the family of modern nations. Article twelve of the document provided that, after the signing by the President of the United States and the Emperor of Japan, and ratification by the United States Senate, the treaty would be in immediate and binding force.

The Commodore returned to the *Powhatan* and summoned Ah Sum to a game of cards.

The Chinese stared at him in amazement. "I am surprised, sir," he said. "Today you have changed the destiny of the Orient, even that of the world. And yet you do not retire by yourself to ponder your greatness, but call this unworthy scholar to share with you a frivolous pastime."

The Commodore grinned. "Ah Sum, today has taught me a lesson. It isn't the man who's important, but the events he puts into motion. For years I have taken myself too seriously and not enjoyed myself enough. Life is too short for complete sobriety. Beginning today, I intend to make up for lost time."

Ten days after the treaty was signed, on April 9, the *Powhatan* departed Yedo Bay with eight warships of the squadron. The *Saratoga* and the *Macedonian* had left several days before, the former bound for Washington with a copy of the treaty, the latter headed for the Bonin Islands for a final survey. The *Plymouth* had weighed anchor for Simoda, to take soundings for the American ships now entitled to dock there.

175

On his way to the Lew Chews the Commodore stopped at Nagasaki, Hokadate and Simoda. Everywhere the Japanese were polite and friendly, and he was able to take a number of inland trips. The charm and natural beauty of the Japanese countryside delighted him. The banquets in his honor proved a little wearisome, but he managed to pick up presents for the family and several valuable objets d'art for American museums.

In late June the squadron arrived in Napha harbor. Leaving it a month later, the Commodore took with him a treaty, signed by the Regent, allowing the establishment of an American coaling station and permitting the right of trade for all American ships putting into the island port. The treaty was the result of hard work, much argument over details, and more of the pomp and ceremony that had so dazzled the Japanese at Yedo.

Macao had heard of the Commodore's success, and waiting for him there were consular representatives of every nation which had commercial interests in the Far East. He was feted at banquet after banquet, and the American merchants of the coast took up a collection to buy him a magnificent silver candelabra of oriental design.

"From the woman's point of view," he wrote Jane joshingly, "the candelabra undoubtedly makes the expedition worthwhile."

Relieved from duty as commander of the Asiatic squadron, the Commodore bought passage on an English steamer bound for Liverpool via Delhi. He had already said goodbye to Oliver, who had left for home from Macao. That night he made his farewell to Ah Sum.

He shook the Chinese's hand warmly. "Ah Sum, I don't know how I'll get along without you. Now I'll have to make my decisions by myself."

There were tears in Ah Sum's eyes. "You joke, Commodore.

Ah Sum was only the unworthy messenger boy of a very great man who deserves much honor from his country. Why did you not go home with your fleet, so that you might receive honors in the proper way?"

Commodore Perry smiled tiredly. "I need a rest, my friend. And for a while I want the anonymity a private citizen enjoys."

The officer who entered the Commodore's cabin a few moments after Ah Sum had left found him dabbing at his eyes with his handkerchief. "A speck in my eye," the Commodore explained gruffly.

Several weeks later private Citizen Perry appeared at the office of Nathaniel Hawthorne, United States Consul in Liverpool, but better known as the author of *Twice Told Tales* and *The House of the Seven Gables*.

Hawthorne was surprised. "Commodore, why aren't you in London, meeting the King? I'm sure the English would want to give you all kinds of receptions and state banquets."

"I have more important business here. Mr. Hawthorne, I'd like your help in preparing the report of the Japanese expedition for the American public."

The great author shook his head in genuine dismay. "Much as I would like to share the by-line with you on so important a document, I'm afraid I cannot. My commitments are such that I wouldn't be free to work with you on the report for another eight months at least."

The Commodore bit his lip. "I'm disappointed. Is there anyone else you can recommend?"

"Yes. The Reverend Francis Hawkes, of New York City."

The Commodore took down the Reverend's name and address. "I shall get in touch with him. Thank you, Mr. Hawthorne, and my own regrets we shan't be working together."

The Commodore's only reason for coming to England was

to enlist Hawthorne's aid in his literary project, and he spent only a brief time in London, moving on quickly to The Hague, to see his daughter Caroline and his son-in-law August Belmont, American Minister to the Netherlands. From the Dutch capital he sailed on the passenger steamer *Baltic* for New York.

A huge crowd of reporters, government officials and important merchants greeted him at the Battery on January 12, 1855. He had to fight his way down the gangplank to the arms of his wife.

"Cal," she said, "you've lost weight!" The wifely greeting, delivered to a husband who, engaged in a history-making task, had been away from her side for a period of more than two years, made all the nation's newspapers.

In 1855 Broadway had no ticker-tape parades, but the Commodore was lionized as had been few heroes before him. There was a constant round of newspaper interviews, receptions and banquets, and he was forced to sit through more congratulatory addresses by leading citizens than the bravest hero could be expected to stomach.

From New York he and Jane moved on to Washington, where a huge state dinner was given for him, attended by President Buchanan, members of the Cabinet, and every foreign ambassador in the capital.

The Chinese embassy sent a huge cake across whose top was a message written in white icing in their language. The Chinese Ambassador translated, "To the Great Commodore, the Opener of Japan." The guests rose in a spontaneous ovation, and from that moment on Matthew Calbraith Perry was known not only to his contemporaries, but to history, as the man who had opened Nippon to the West.

In Boston a special medal was struck off in his honor, and there was another round of banquets. With a certain amount of relief he and Jane left for an outdoor reception at Newport

178

in his home state of Rhode Island. It was there, on the balcony facing the old state house, that he delivered the brief speech which almost everyone, young and old, in the packed audience, found deeply affecting.

He spoke of his boyhood, and he spoke of the Navy, too:

"It was in my earliest boyhood, before any of us ever dreamed of steamboats or railroads, that I stood often on the Narragansett shore, waiting for the first glimpse of that gaily decorated packet sloop that in those days brought the governor from Providence to Newport. I watched with the delight of a child, in the sight of this very building, the pomp and parade of 'Election Day.' Since that time I have traveled almost every part of the globe in behalf of a profession of which I am justly proud, and now, after almost half a century has passed, and youth is no longer youth but age, it is an honor to be called by the Governor back to these green shores, to receive here from its chief magistrate the commendation of my fellow citizens. It is an honor I little expected when, as a boy midshipman forty-six years ago, I first entered the Navy. It is an honor I will never forget."

Later reporters crowded around to ask about his future plans. Was he going to take another command? An ambassadorship? Would he buy a farm in his native Rhode Island and retire?

The aging sea dog's eyes twinkled. "Boys, these days I don't plan further than my nose. Just now I'm going to take a tramp over the Narragansett countryside, and see if old Burr Lowrey, the blacksmith, is still alive, and if Granny Abbott still makes that delicious ice cream."

But he did have long-range plans. Most important was the huge task of writing the final report of the Japanese expedition. It would take at least a year of toil, sifting over the correspondence, his own handwritten journals, the account of Bayard Taylor, and many of the journals kept by his officers.

There was also a trunk full of special reports on Japanese geography, flora and fauna. And he would have to go through hundreds of sketches and color plates with Heine and Brown, the official artists of the expedition. Neither the house at Tarrytown nor his recently purchased New York brownstone was suitable for the work involved, and he decided to take lodgings in Washington. Reverend Hawkes arrived from New York to help with the editorial work.

In 1856 the *Narrative of the Expedition of an American Squadron to the China Seas and Japan* was published by Act of Congress. It consisted of three fat volumes totaling nearly fifteen hundred pages, and included several hundred color plates and charts. The first volume contained the day by day record of the expedition from the sailing of the *Mississippi* from Norfolk to the return of the *Powhatan* to Macao. Volume two was made up of scientific reports by Bayard Taylor and various hands in the Lew Chews and Japan. The third volume was devoted to astronomical observations made at sea by one of the chaplains of the squadron.

Fifteen thousand copies were printed and paid for by a Congressional appropriation of $360,000. Ten thousand copies were distributed free among the Congressmen, and another two thousand were sent to the Navy Department. Of the thousand copies he was given as a gift, the Commodore turned over five hundred to Reverend Hawkes. The Commander of the Japanese expedition received no other recompense.

He felt no bitterness over that—a Navy man could expect no financial rewards for serving his country above and beyond the call of duty. But he did feel slighted by reports that he was being criticized at Washington dinner parties for the style of volume one. People were amused by the fact that it was written in the third person, rather than the first. They

180

were calling him the most pompous author who had ever published a fifteen hundred page book.

"It makes me furious!" he stormed to Jane. "Here I was, trying to play myself down, and they call me arrogant and vain! Will I never understand the world outside a ship of the line?"

Jane smoothed her husband's still unruly hair. "Now Cal," she said soothingly, "I was talking to Mrs. Buchanan just today, and she told me she found your observations and descriptions of Japanese life simply fascinating. And didn't that Professor Wilson say your *Narrative* had tremendous historical importance, and that no scholar would be able to write a book on the Orient who hadn't read it first?"

The Commodore grinned, somewhat mollified. "Forgive me, my dear, I'm acting like an author. Sailors should never act like authors. The literary seas are too rough for them."

Before he left Washington, the Commodore arranged for disposal of the Emperor's various gifts. The Smithsonian Institution was glad to take most of them, including the textiles and the Japanese dolls.

In Brooklyn the Commodore took over command of the Navy yard, and formally raised the broad pennant and hauled it down again, signifying the end of the Japanese cruise. Waiting for him at his new house on West 32nd Street in Manhattan was a letter from his old Tarrytown neighbor, Washington Irving. Thanking the Commodore for the copy of the *Narrative* he had sent him, Irving went on to say:

You have gained for yourself a lasting name and have won it without shedding a drop of blood or inflicting misery on one human being. What naval commander ever won laurels at such a rate?

The Commodore thought of his brother Oliver. Oliver Hazard Perry had been the greatest naval hero of his time. Had he, with his own achievements, outdistanced him? He dropped the thought. As young Ol had said, Let posterity decide.

A few months after taking over his old command, a severe attack of rheumatism laid him low, and he went to Saratoga Springs for the mineral baths. There a doctor gave him a piece of bad news. The rheumatism had affected his heart. He had better slow down, or there would be serious complications.

"You're doing too much," the doctor warned him. "All this commuting between New York and Washington is bad for you."

"Doctor, you can't refuse your government when they ask you for advice."

"Will you at least promise to cut down on your activities?"

The Commodore grinned. "All right, if you'll permit me a little politics."

"Politics! There's nothing like politics to kill a man!"

"In a small way I'm a candidate for office. A group of merchants are urging my appointment as American Commissioner to China."

The doctor shook his head. "For your own sake I hope you fail to get it."

As it worked out, another man received the appointment through a misunderstanding at the State Department. The Commodore was not too disappointed; Jane hadn't wanted him to go to China in the first place; and another Perry had packed his bags for the Orient—Oliver Hazard was appointed Consul at Shanghai.

That fall the Commodore was guest of honor at a dinner given for him at Delmonico's by the Mayor of New York, Fernando Wood. The company was distinguished: present were General Winfield Scott, Martin Van Buren, Washington Irving, and a dozen other notables. As usual the Commodore was the least talkative man at the table, while General Scott waxed particularly loquaciously. Finally Irving turned to the Commodore and said, "There is too much silence from the quarter-deck, Commodore Perry. When are you going to uphold the honor of the Navy by stealing some of General Scott's thunder?"

The Commodore replied, "Washington, that would be difficult, since I have already loaned the General all my big guns."

A society columnist for one of the New York newspapers commented the next day that the Commodore had won the verbal engagement with a "Vera Cruz salvo that was heard as far as the Battery."

Townsend Harris, appointed by President Buchanan to the post of First American Consul at Simoda, came to the house on 32nd Street to ask the Commodore's advice on handling the Japanese.

"You won't have an easy time of it," Commodore Perry warned him. "The Japanese will fight you at every turn with procrastination, evasion and subterfuge. You'll feel like you're swimming in a great tub of molasses, with no prospect of getting safely out. But if you stand firm and refuse to compromise on the smallest matters, the big ones will take care of themselves."

"But sir," Harris protested, "we've signed a treaty. Japan is bound to honor it."

"Mr. Harris, you will learn that when an Oriental signs a treaty he keeps his fingers crossed, his eyes, and sometimes even his ankles."

Over a year later the Commodore received a letter from Harris:

I am much obliged to you for your good advice. It was both sound and well-timed, and I have found every one of your opinions, as to the course the Japanese would pursue with me, proved true to the letter. . . . For fully ten months the Japanese used every possible expedient to get me to deliver the President's letter at Shimado and to make my communications to the governors of this place. I steadily refused to do either. . . . Next month I shall start for Yedo, where I am to have an audience with the Emperor. I will deliver the letter at that time.

I have just obtained a copy of your Expedition to Japan and the China Seas and have read it with intense interest. I hope it is no vanity in me to say that no one at present can so well appreciate and do justice to your work. . . . You seem at once and almost intuitively to have adopted the best of all courses with the Japanese.

Early in 1859 the Commodore was appointed to the command of the Mediterranean squadron, the plum he had waited for all his life, and one particularly appropriate now that he needed a warmer climate for his chronic rheumatism. His flagship was scheduled to leave for Port Mahon in April, and in late February he took to his bed with another attack of rheumatism. It was a severe one, but around the first of March he was well enough to sit in his library armchair with a copy of his book on the Japanese expedition.

It was there that Jane found him on midnight of the fourth of March. The heart of Matthew Calbraith Perry had stopped beating and the Great Commodore was dead.

A day later his body was laid to rest in the Slidell family vault at St. Mark's-in-the-Bouwerie on Second Avenue in New York. In the funeral cortege were five hundred men of the 7th United States Infantry, a battalion of United States Marines, and two hundred officers of the New York State

Militia. Among the pallbearers were General Scott, John Jay, and four Commodores of the Navy. But these were not the only men who marched in the Commodore's last parade down Fifth and Second Avenues to the Episcopal Church. Many of the ordinary bluejackets who had sailed with him to Japan marched in civilian clothes and old uniforms to do their dead chief honor. They had loved him better than he knew.

There was no funeral oration, as by express wish of the Commodore himself. No illustrious contemporary stood up to list his chief accomplishments: co-founder of Liberia, scourge of pirates, pioneer of naval sanitation, Father of the Steam Navy, victor with Winfield Scott at Vera Cruz, the opener of Japan. There was no one to say that here, dead at sixty-four, lay one of our greatest Americans.

But Matthew Calbraith Perry wanted it that way. He was a modest man.

BIBLIOGRAPHY

American Colonization Society. *Annual Reports.* Washington: American Colonization Society, 1854.

Ashmun, Jehudi. *Condition of the Colony at Liberia.* Washington: American Colonization Society, 1828.

——. *History of the American Colony in Liberia.* Washington: Way & Gideon, 1826.

Barrows, Edward M. *The Great Commodore.* Indianapolis: The Bobbs-Merrill Co., 1935.

Dutton, Charles J. *Oliver Hazard Perry.* New York: Longmans, Green & Co., 1935.

Griffis, William E. *Japanese Nation in Evolution.* New York: Thomas Y. Crowell Co., 1907.

——. *Matthew Calbraith Perry.* Boston: Cupples & Hurd, 1887.

——. *The Mikado's Empire.* New York: Harper & Brothers, 1883.

——. *Townsend Harris.* Boston: Houghton Mifflin Co., 1895.

Harris, Townsend. *Complete Journal.* New York: Doubleday and Co., 1930.

Hawkes, Reverend Francis L. *Narrative of the Japanese Expedition of an American Squadron to the China Seas and Japan. Compiled from the Original Notes and Documents of Commodore Perry and His Officers.* Washington: 33rd Congress, 2nd Session, S. ec. doc. No. 79.

Kuhn Ferdinand. *Commodore Perry and The Opening of Japan.* New York: Random House, 1955.

Long, Laura. *Square Sails and Spice Islands.* New York: Longmans, Green & Co., 1945.

Mackenzie, Alexander Slidell. *Life of Oliver Hazard Perry.* New York: Harper & Brothers, 1840.

Naval Magazine. Washington: United States Naval Lyceum, 1837.

Semmes, Raphael. *Service Afloat and Ashore During the Mexican War.* Cincinnati: W. H. Moore, 1851.

Taylor, Bayard. *A Visit to India, China and Japan.* New York: G. P. Putnam's Sons, 1855.

Walworth, Arthur C. Black Ships Off Japan. New York: Alfred A. Knopf, Inc., 1946.

INDEX

Acachapan, Mexico, 112
Africa, 43-47, 49-58, 65, 92-102
Ah Sum, 124-26, 133, 135, 137, 141-
    44, 147, 148-50, 154-58, 161-62,
    163, 165, 167-70, 173-75, 176-77
Alaska, 12, 114
Algiers, 67
Alvarado, Mexico, 104
American/s, 11, 15-16, 23, 25, 34,
    36, 40, 42-43, 58, 67, 74, 76-77,
    79, 94, 114-16, 118-20
American Colonization Society, 44-
    47, 53-55
Amherstburg, 32
Amsterdam, Holland, 42
Annapolis, naval academy at, 102
Antilles, the, 58
Argus, the, 26
armaments, naval, Perry's ideas on,
    81, 84-85, 88
Ashmun, Reverend Jehudi, 44-47, 53-
    55, 56-58, 92
Asia, 114
Athens, Greece, 67
Atlanta, the, 94
Atlantic Coast squadron, 21
Atlantic Ocean, 114
Aulick, Commodore J. H., 116-17,
    121
Austria, Emperor of, 69
Ayres, Dr. Eli, 56

Baltic, the, 178
Barbary Coast, 40, 76
Barclay, Captain, 32
Batavia, 161
Belmont, August, 178
Belvidera, the, 25-28
Beribi, 93, 99-101

Bering Straits, 73
Bettelheim, Reverend, 129-33, 134
Biddle, Commodore, 115
Bingham, Captain, 25
Bomba, King, 78-79
Bonaparte, Joseph, 77
Bonin Islands, 137, 175
Boston, Massachusetts, 28-29, 30, 34,
    41, 42, 44, 178
Boston, the, 79
Brandywine, the, 78
Bravas, General, 105-06, 112
Brazos Island, 107
Bristol, Rhode Island, 70
British, 15-16, 23-28, 31-32, 34, 35,
    39, 41, 66, 67, 83, 92, 115, 129,
    137, 161, 177
Brooklyn, New York, 80, 181
Buchanan, Captain, 144-47, 148-49,
    153, 158-59, 163-66
Buchanan, President, 178
Bushmen, the, 93-99

California, 103, 114, 116, 121
Canton, China, 127
Cape Henry, 122
Cape Idsu, 140
Cape Mesurado, 45, 46, 56
Cape Palmas, 93, 97, 99, 102
Cape Prince of Wales, 12
Cape Verde, 46, 92
Cape of Sugami, 141
Capetown, 122
Caprice, the, 138
"cat," use of, 72-73
Ceylon, 124
Chelsea, the, 41-42
Chesapeake Bay, 23, 121
Chesapeake, the, 16, 25

187

China, 116, 119, 122, 123, 127, 160, 167, 178, 182
China Seas, 115, 118
Chippewa, the, 38
Civil War, 77
Columbia River, 115
Concord, the, 71-80
Congress, the, 26
Congress, U. S., 16, 36, 44-45, 79, 116, 127, 180
Conner, Commodore David, 104-05, 107-08, 109, 117
Constantine, the, 160
Cook, Captain, 11-12
Copenhagen, Denmark, 76
Corinth, Greee, 67-68
Cowes, 76
Cuba, 58, 64
Cummings, Everett, 77
Cyane, the, 45-47, 50-55

Devil's Elbow, 110
Disovery, The, 11-12
Dutch, 115, 146-47, 161, 171, 178

East River, 81
Elizabeth, the, 45-46
Emperor, the. *See* Mikado, the
English. *See* British
Erie, the, 67
Europe, 76, 84, 114, 160
Everglades, 58-63

Far East, 114, 176
Farragut, Lieutenant David, 104
Favorite, H. M. S., 39
Fillmore, President Millard, 120, 154-56
Fishmen, the, 93-102
Flordia, 58, 60-64
French, 66, 83, 115, 160
Frontera, Mexico, 105
Fulton 1st, the, 85-86
Fulton II, 87-90
Fulton, Robert, 41, 85-86

Germany, 77
Ghent, Treaty of, 39
Gibraltar, 69

Gifford, Midshipman, 28
Glynn, Captain, 115-16
Gold Coast, 45, 47, 49, 92-102
Gorihama, 149, 151
Graham, Navy Secretary, 116-17, 119
Greece, 67-68
Guerriere, the, 23

Hakodate, Japan, 171, 176
Harris, Townsend, 183-84
Havre de Grace, Maryland, 23
Hawkes, Reverend Francis, 117, 180
Hawthorne, Nathaniel, 177
Heidelberg, 77
Holland, 41-42
Hong Kong, 126-27, 138, 161

Irving, Washington, 82, 181, 183
Isle of Wight, 76
Iyesada, Shogun, 162-63

Jackson, President, 71, 78
Japan, 114, 116, 118-20, 122, 131, 138, 153, 160, 162-63, 167, 172, 183
Japanese, 114-19, 125, 131-38, 140-59, 161-76, 183-84
Jay, John, 185
Jenks, Alfred, 73-75, 80
Jersey, the, 17
John Adams, the, 43, 79
Johnson, James, 19-21

Kama-Kura, 164-65
Kamou, Princess, 76-77
Kanagawa, 165
Kennedy, John P., 120, 122
King Ben, 100-01
King Freeman, 93
King George, 95
King Nippio, 96-97
Kronstadt, Russia, 71-73
Kroomen, the, 94-96

Lake Erie, battle of, 32
Lee, Captain Robert E., 109
Leopard H.M.S., 16
Levant, the, 65, 67, 76
Lew Chew islands, 122-23, 129-38, 159, 171-72, 176

Liberia, 44-47, 53-55, 56-58, 92-93, 99
Little Belt, H.M.S., 24-25
Liverpool, England, 177
London, England, 76
Long Island, 18, 89
"Lord of the Forbidden Interior," 119, 126, 142-44, 152
Lyceum, the, 82

Macao, 116, 118, 121, 127, 159-60, 176
Macedonian, the, 67, 118, 175
Madeira Islands, 122
Madison, President, 25
Marston, Lieutenant, 59-63
Mary Carver, the, 94-97, 99-102
Maryland, 23
Maryland Colonization Society, 93
Mauritius, 122, 124
Mediterranean Sea, 65-70, 76-79
Mediterranean squadron, 65-70, 184
Mesurado River, 54
Mexico, 102-03, 104-13
Mexico City, 102, 113
Mikado, the, 116, 118-19, 125, 131, 168, 173-74
Minorca, 65
Mississippi, the, 90, 105, 107-08, 118, 122-24, 126, 143, 147-48, 168
Missouri, the, 90
Molucca, Strait of, 124
Monrovia, 92, 102
Montauk Point, 18
Morgan, Captain Charles, 65, 67
Morrison, the, 115, 123
Moslems, 67-68, 76
"Mosquito Fleet," 59
Mount Fujiyama, 40

Nagasaki, 115, 116, 144, 146, 171, 176
Nantucket Shoals, 18, 25
Napha, 129-38, 159, 161, 171, 176
Naples, 77-79
Narragansett Bay, 11, 32
Narrative of the Expedition of an American Squadron to the China Seas and Japan, 179-81

Naval Magazine, 82
Navy Department, 17, 41, 42, 43, 45, 55, 70, 74, 80-81, 84, 86-88, 104, 115, 180
Nelson, John, 78-79
Netherlands, the, 178, *See also* Dutch, Holland
New London, Conecticut, 89
New Mexico, 103
New Orleans, Louisiana, 107, 113
New York City, 18, 23, 39, 41, 55, 58, 67, 85, 88, 91, 118, 178, 181, 182
New York *Herald*, 120-21
New York Navy Yard, 80-82, 181
Newport, Rhode Island, 11, 12, 15, 25, 32, 58, 178-79
Nipponese. *See* Japanese
Norfolk, the, 13
Norfolk, Virginia, 72, 107, 121
North Carolina, the, 65, 67-70
Norway, 31

officer training, naval, Perry's ideas on, 66, 71, 80, 82
Okinawa, 129
Oregon, 114

Pacific Ocean, 114
Patras, Greece, 67
Patterson, Commodore John, 77-79
Patterson, General, 107
Paulding, J. K., 89
Perry, Alexander (brother), 35, 36 58
Perry, Caroline (daughter), 67, 91, 178
Perry, Christopher (father), 14, 15-17, 21, 25, 33
Perry, Elizabeth (sister-in-law), 34, 36
Perry, Jane (daughter), 67, 91
Perry, Jane (sister), 15, 32, 72
Perry, Jane Slidell (wife), 34-36, 41-42, 46, 55, 70-72, 79-80, 107, 113, 118-19, 120-21, 128, 176, 178, 181, 184. *Se also* Slidell, Jane
Perry, John Slidell (son), 42, 46

Perry, Matthew Calbraith, at 13, 11-17; as midshipman, 18-33; in first battle, 24; is wounded, 26; is assigned to recruiting, 29; meets Jane, 29-30; commissioned junior lieutenant, 33; marriage, 34; he and Oliver still do not get along, 35, 37, 43; on recruitment duty, 37-40; death of father, 41; envisions steam navy, 41; in merchant service, 41-42; birth of son, 42; feels Navy could help American commerce, 42-43; becomes interested in new African colony, 43-44; is member of expedition, 45; birth of second child, 46; death of son John, 46; death of brother Oliver, 47; in Africa, 49-55, 56-58; makes recommendations on sanitation and hygiene, 55-56, 70; deaths of brother Alexander and mother, 58; in action against Everglades pirates, 58-64; birth of third child, 65; is promoted to lieutenant commander, 65; his ideas for officer training, 66, 71, 80; with Mediterranean squadron, 67-70; birth of twin daughters, 67; is ill with rheumatism, 69; appointed acting Master Commandant, 69; death of brother Raymond, 70; to Russia, 71-76; his ideas on steam navy, 74, 80-90; on diplomatic mission to Naples, 78-79; commands New York Navy Yard, 81; moves to Tarrytown, 81; other projects, 82; is promoted to captain, 83; interests Navy in new arms, 84; two of his sons midshipmen, 85; builds the Fulton II, 87-90; is Father of the Steam Navy, 90; is promoted to Commodore, 91; to Africa again, 92-102; in war with Mexico, 104-13; commands Japanese expedition, 117-76; other countries emulating his success, 160-61; finally discusses treaty, 170-72, 175; secures Napha treaty, 176; voyage home, 176-77; honors, 178;
writes report of expedition, 179-80; is ill, 182, death, 184
Perry, Matthew Calbraith, Jr. (son), 46, 55, 72, 85-87, 104-05
Perry, Oliver Hazard (brother), 12, 14, 18-20, 28, 32-33, 34, 35-41, 43, 47-48, 83, 91, 139, 182
Perry, Oliver Hazard (son), 65, 72, 85-86, 104, 121, 127, 128, 139-40, 171, 176, 182
Perry, Raymond (brother), 13, 21, 23, 25, 35-36, 39-41, 70
Perry, Sarah (mother), 15, 58
Philadelphia Navy Yard, 90
Philadelphia, Pennsylvania, 77, 118
Pickering, Lieutenant, 89-90
pirates, 40, 58-64, 67, 76
Plymouth, the, 126-27, 140, 142, 175
Point Judith, 11, 32
Polk, President, 102
Porpoise, the, 94
Port Mahon, 65, 69-70, 77, 184
Porter, Commodore David, 58-60, 64
Portsmouth, 79
Portuguese territory in Africa, 52-53
Powhatan, the, 122, 163, 166, 175
Preble, the, 115
President, the, 21-28, 31-32, 34
Prince Akhito, 135
Prince Ido, 154-58
Prince Joe, 93
Prince John, 95
Prince Jumbo, 94
Prince Toda, 149, 154-58
Princeton, the, 118, 121-22
Providence, Rhode Island, 12

Randolph, John, 71, 72-73, 76
Raritan, the, 104
Revenge, the, 18-21
Revolutionary War, 14, 17
Rhode Island, 12, 21, 37, 70
Rio de Janeiro, 116
Roberts, President, 92-93
Rockboukir, 100
Rodgers, Commodore Samuel, 21-29, 31-35, 65-66, 67-70

Rotterdam, Holland, 41
Russia, 71-76, 160-61

Sacrificios Island, 104, 106
St. Marks-in-the-Bouwerie, 92, 184
Saint Petersburg, Russia, 71, 74
San Francisco, California, 116
San Juan Bautista, Mexico, 105-06, 110-13
Sanders, Lieutenant, 25, 27
Sandy Hook, 84, 88, 102
Sandwich Islands, 12
sanitation, naval, Perry's ideas on, 55-56, 70
Santa Anna, General, 110
Saranac, the, 38
Saratoga Springs, New York, 182
Saratoga, the, 92-102, 104, 111, 118, 126, 174, 175
Scott, General Winfield, 106-09, 113, 183, 185
scurvy, 52, 55-56
Shanghai, 126, 138, 182
Shark, the, 56, 58, 64
Sherbro, 46-47, 53-54
Sherman, Commodore, 82-83
Shogun, the, 126, 161-3
Shudi, 132, 136
Siberia, 12
Simoda, Japan, 171, 175, 176, 183
Singapore, 124
Sinoe, 97-98
slave trade, 44, 49-52, 92
Slidell, George, 24, 29-30, 32
Slidell, Jane, 29-31, 33. *See also* Perry, Jane
smallpox, 70
Smithsonian Institution, 181
Smyrna, 68
South America, 43, 116
Spain, 66
Spitfire, the, 110
State Department, 43, 72, 76, 114, 116, 123, 137, 182
steam Navy, Perry's ideas on, 41-42, 74, 80-81, 83-90; in 1845, 103
Supply, the, 118, 126, 138
Susquehanna, the, 116, 118, 126, 131, 137-38, 140, 146, 159

Tabasco River, 105, 110
Tampico, Mexico, 107
Tangier, 67
Tarrytown, New York, 81, 85, 107, 118
Taylor, Bayard, 128-29
Taylor, President Zachary, 116, 120
Teneriffe, 52-53, 92
Texas, 102-03
Tokyo. *See* Yedo Bay
Tompkins, Adam, 160
Trenchard, Captain, 45-47, 50-55
Trieste, 69
Trinidad, 47
Tripoli, 40, 43
tropical fever, 47, 52, 55-56, 92, 104
Trumbull, the, 14
Tsar Nicholas, 73-75
Tunis, 67, 76
Turks, 67-68
Tuxpan, Mexico, 110

United States, 49, 53, 67, 79, 86, 95, 102-03, 113, 114, 128, 136, 137, 144, 149, 155
United States, the, 26, 79
U. S. Army, 106-10
U. S. Navy, 13-14, 16-17, 18, 21-28, 29, 31-32, 34-41, 42, 45-46, 50-64, 65-70, 71-90, 91, 92, 102-03, 104-13, 115-76, 184
Uruga, Japan, 142, 146, 149, 151, 158-59, 165

Valparaiso, Chile, 58
Van Buren, President Martin, 89, 183
Vandalia, the, 118
Venezuela, 43
Vera Cruz, Mexico, 58-59, 64, 104, 107-10, 113
Vermont, the, 118
Virginia, 71, 72
Vixen, the, 106

War of 1812, 25-28, 31-39, 45
Warren, Edgar, 29-30
Warren, Rhode Island, 37

191

Washington, D.C., 69, 88, 89, 107, 116, 119, 122, 175, 178
Watt, the, 14
Webster, Daniel, 116, 119-20
Webster, Noah, 11-12
West Indies, 58
Wood, Mayor Fernando, 182

Yedo, 146-47, 158, 163, 165
Yedo Bay, 115, 144, 148, 175
Yedo Harbor, 140, 165
Yokohama, 168

Zanzibar, 116
Zellin, Major, 153

About the Author

ARTHUR ORRMONT was born in
Albany, New York, moved to Brooklyn
where he graduated from Erasmus Hall
High School. Interested in writing from
the age of twelve, he attended the Uni-
versity of Michigan, where he was a three-
time winner of the Avery Hopwood
award in creative writing. After graduate
work at Cornell, he came to New York
and entered the book publishing field
where he remained for the next twelve
years. He resigned as executive editor of
a large publishing firm in 1957, and is
now doing free-lance writing of short
stories, magazine articles and books, both
adult and juvenile.